Cross Town Route

Cross Town Route

Katie B. Catalon

TO SOW IS TO HARVEST

Scythe Publications, Inc.
A Division of Winston-Derek Publishers Group, Inc.

PUBLISHED BY SCYTHE PUBLICATIONS, INC.
A Division of Winston-Derek Publishers Group, Inc.
Nashville, Tennessee 37205

Library of Congress Catalog Card No: 94-60120
ISBN: 1-55523-678-2

Printed in the United States of America

For
Dida Mansfield Bell,
my dear mother

Daisy B. Brockington,
my dear sister,
for all the words of encouragement

Allen Paul, my husband,
for the gift of the computer

Introduction

I begin by saying that I hope that I will not have to offer anyone an apology, because what I have written was not done in a way to ridicule anyone or any particular city. For many years I rode this particular bus route and talked with and enjoyed the wonderful people that were riding the bus. No doubt, if anyone else were to write about the passengers that rode this bus, I could very well be one of the passengers to write about.

I saw many women in the coldest of winter and the hottest heat of summer struggling from day to day trying to make ends meet. They were proud people and worked very hard for the small wages received for a day's work. Some of the women were so old, I wondered how they would make it through the day. To receive a welfare check as long as a body could work was unheard of. A part of whatever was received in wages for the day would be left in a corner store for making a meal for the family that night.

There were days when it rained so hard, and many did not have an umbrella to keep from getting wet. There were times that their feet would be covered by water by the time the bus would arrive. Yet, they came on the bus with a determination in their eyes that they were going to make another day.

I became a part of them by riding the bus. They became my friends, and at each bus stop I always expected to see the usual individuals get on the bus. I knew right away when one was ill, and I felt sadness when death claimed one. I also sensed a loss. In fact, everyone who rode the bus experienced a loss.

I took note of the word out on the bus that, if anyone had a relative who needed the job when one of the day workers died, all they had to do was to talk to a lady named Minnie, who had been riding the bus for many years. She would steer the person on to the job. I guess one could call Minnie an employment agency.

She knew everything about everybody that rode that bus. I guess that the only reason she did not know much about me is that I was already on the bus when she got on. But she made it a point to look me in the eye every day and say "Morning". I always smiled and answered back with a loud "Good morning". Then, I would settle back in my seat and watch Minnie begin her interaction with the other people getting on the bus.

It seemed as if everyone had a particular seat on the bus, and no one sat in anyone else's seat. It was just taken for granted by all that was the way it would be.

It appeared to me that the lady named Minnie was a leader. Everyday I would listen to her talk. She knew about the personalities of every house the other ladies worked in. Many of them were not treated kindly in some of the homes, but through it all, they found time to laugh and to make others laugh.

Each day I rode the bus, I was drawn a little more into their circle. I liked to hear them talk. I saw them in a special way. They were going to work and I was going to work, and just because my type of work was different from theirs made me no better than them. The only difference I could tell was that I was only thirty years old, and the majority of them had the age to be my grandmother. I saw them in a special way, and I enjoyed riding the bus with them. I fell in love with them because they were my people.

The most interesting time to ride the bus was on Monday morning. Everyone would catch up on the weekend gossip. When everyone got on the bus the previous Friday, the conversation was which church had a revival going and if the minister was going to get a new car. But on Mondays it was: who was going with who; how many funerals were held; who got married; who had a baby;

who was caught with someone other than the husband or the wife; who went to jail; and who was getting a divorce.

They always enjoyed these talks. Nothing they talked about was a secret. The passengers were from different neighborhoods, and all of the information just came together by word of mouth. Some had been printed in the newspaper. Some was heard on radio, and some saw it on the television. If you missed all three, then you got it on the bus. However, as the bus pulled to a stop to let off the passengers, a different look would come onto the many faces. The gaiety would cease, and with solemn expressions, they would exit from the bus.

One day, I caught the bus at the stop where the lady named Minnie always caught it. I was getting my car on that day, and it would be my last time riding the bus. Minnie was angry because the bus was very late. I was cold and quite uncomfortable standing there, but somehow I was warmed a bit by hearing Minnie's voice.

Dear Jesus, I am sixty-seven years old today, and looking back, Lord, I ain't got no more now than what I started with years ago. Then too, Lord, I ain't lost nothing either. I got a place to stay, food to eat, there's Momma and the children; we all has clothes to wear. Lord, you done blessed us all with good health. So you hear, Lord, I ain't complaining. This is just my way of thanking you, Lord, for blessing me and mine.

I wonder why this bus so late this morning. Could be Bessie son driving again today. When he first started on this route, he would be on time. Just because he been on the job for a year or two, I sure hope he don't mess up like that other driver. He sure should have known better. I wonder why he did not drive the bus back to the bus yard after his route. He sure been a fool for taking that young school girl and stopping in the woods on the way back to the bus yard.

I thought that look like you coming from up the street, Janie. How things going with you over at the hospital?

Yeah, girl, I guess you got a point there. But you know, I always did say, it ain't them that got them degrees is always the smart ones. What gets me is when your own people looks down on you. As I can recall you been working over there a long time. I been riding this bus over twenty-three years, and things ain't no better now than then. Sure, we can sit anywhere we want to, but these children getting on this bus after school ain't got no manners. We use to ride this bus with dignity. We respected each other. But now, they gets on this bus and plays them boxes so loud we don't hear what we saying any more.

Go on girl and tell me what the teacher say when she come to the hospital to get her girl.

So, she don't want her child touched by no emergency room doctor? I bet she sure was surprised when she got there and found out she left home that morning a momma and a teacher and found out at the hospital she be a momma, teacher, and grand-momma all in one day. Janie, I bet you see and know a lot going on in that old hospital.

Is that a new coat you got on? Sure don't look like you had it that long. I guess I just never paid attention to it before. Looks heavy on you, too. Need a heavy coat on a morning like this one. Sure hope the bus ain't broke down.

You never did finish telling me about Dr. Hatton that time. A person just don't want to believe that a person can be such a fool. He such a fool to believe that the yard man was in the mud room with no clothes on 'cause he spill that stuff all over his self, and then he hears Mrs. Hatton falling all the way up stairs, and he just runs up there with no clothes on to see what done happen to her.

Oh yeah, she faint alright. I bet she faint after Dr. Hatton come in and caught them together. So when she not faint no more, she tell the doctor she wake up and see a man in her room and she yell for help, and that be the time when the yard man come to her room? It just so happen that be the time the doctor come home one day early from that seminar thing he go to every year. I guess you know what you talking bout when you say that Dr. Hatton smart in one way, but sure dumb in the common sense way.

Here come Jessie. Morning Jessie. How your boy doing? Oh he is, now ain't that good. Well, you know how some peoples children is. Some do, and some don't. Just you keep the faith, girl. If the bus been on time, I would not have seen you today. Who you got a days work with today?

Well you can walk on over there. That ain't too far. See you in church Sunday. Don't forget; we change into the long black robes on Sunday.

Janie, I wonder if Jessie take me for some ol' fool? Smiling and telling me that her boy Joe doing fine. He just been picked up at school for them bad cigarettes again. I said to myself when he

6

done fight her that time and take her food stamps and sell them to that no account Marion; then was the time to do something. Then you tell me how the police done bring her to the hospital, and she tell a big ol' lie that some strange man grab her purse and beat her up. Feel sorry for her. Hear tell she may lose sight in that eye from that same beating. You mean to tell me I gonna feed you, keep clothes on your back and a roof over you head, and you gonna fight me? Your own momma who done birth you in this world? Honey, I be sitting in the jail, but one of mine hit me it sure will be a big funeral, 'cause I got each covered in good insurance. Now a days, honey, you got to make the young ones respect you. They brings home a ball, make 'em take it back. You know you did not buy the ball. You got to stop 'em when they young.

Hey, Pearl. Sure can't take a chance like you being late. Be just my luck for that ol' stupid bus to be on time. I been standing out here over twenty minutes. Just Janie and me. I guess the others got them husbands to take them on the island this morning.

I been over there on Wednesday. I knocked out two in one day. When they just want a good cleaning job, I can do that. I sure don't take too kindly to the ironing along with that there cleaning, though. They got the money, but they try to get two jobs for the price of one.

Mrs. Sears come trying some funny business with me on Monday. She says to me, "Minnie, Mrs. Arnold told me that you did a splendid job on Mr. Arnold's shirts. It would be nice if you would just pitch in and do a few of Mrs. Sears shirts."

I looks her straight in the eyes and says to her, "Mrs. Sears, I iron for Mrs. Arnold on Fridays and cleans for Mrs. Arnold on Wednesdays. Now, if you wants me to iron for you, I will keep coming to you to clean on Mondays and come back to you to iron on Thursdays after I leave from Mrs. Brinson."

Honey, I hushed her up real good.

That sure is strange. Hester, Madge, and Charlotte ain't here yet. Now you take Hester, she like going in today 'cause she be with Mrs. Timmons. Everybody knows Mrs. Timmons must be close to ninety if she ain't a day over. That is a easy day for Hester. Hester got arthritis so bad. Not much she capable of doing. She just good company for Mrs. Timmons. Hester's girl, that one that is teaching in that school in Kentucky, is trying to get Hester to come over there to live with her. Hester went one time. Never could figure why she won't go back. Mrs. Timmons lonely, and Hester lonely. Each one got children right here, and none of them children got time to go to visit with their momma. Sure they picks up the phone and calls at times. Between them calls, a body can be stone cold dead before found.

I just bet Madge is stuck with them grandchildren again. I done told her that, if it was me, I would be walking out of my door when they were walking in with the children. If they would just give her a little something for keeping all of those children, Madge would not have to come and stand on this ol' corner in all this cold weather at her age. Talk about ungrateful children.

Missed her at church last Sunday. Said to her at the grocery store, "Didn't see you at church Sunday. I told Reverend South, 'Sure hope Sister Madge is not sick.' "

That's when she laid it on me. Come telling me that the grands were brought to her on Saturday morning 'cause them girls were going upstate to a concert, and would be back early Sunday morning, and for her not to worry, they would be back in time for her to go to church. Well, they got back on Sunday alright, and it would have been great if Madge had a nine o'clock night service at her church.

Honey, I don't let nobody stand in the way of me and my church. That is why you see me with no husband this day. You remember when I was married to Albert?

What do you mean, I did not stay married long enough for you to remember? I stayed long enough for two children in one year. I lucked out I had twins. The good Lord knew his servant was married to a fool. When Albert got up that Sunday morning to keep me from going to church and wanted to fight me because he said I must be going with the reverend, honey, that was one morning he thought he had locked horns with Satan himself. Janie, you were at the hospital when they brung him in. I give him a grease bath that morning that he will take to his grave, wherever he is.

He ain't never tried to stop me from going to work, and you mean to tell me he that big a fool to try to stop me from going to my church? I may not be book learned like some people, but I got sense. Honey, you don't have to hit me; just raise your hand like you is going to. I know I got his hand, but I never knew about the rest of the body until you told me. And do you know, Janie, I started not to cook the pork chops that morning, but I said to myself on the way home that Friday that I would fix some chops and gravy for a big Sunday breakfast before church.

Girl, I look around and see all these people all beat up and trying to hide the truth. They must be crazy. They need help. What's the name of that doctor at the hospital that beat up his wife, and he got so scared he checked her into the hospital under a different name and put a sign on the door to make people think she had that spreading disease? Saw her picture with him on the society page. Noticed that she has a new baby. Sure could not be me, honey.

Charlotte is indeed a fool. If Charlotte is not forty-seven, I am not standing at this bus stop waiting for a stupid bus with a stupid driver that is over thirty minutes late. I told Charlotte not to be stupid. I am older than her, and I try to treat her like I would a sister. The last time Elmore promised Charlotte that he would be coming into town, he never showed up. Okay. Charlotte did not go to work for three days waiting for Elmore to call her. Finally, he pulls his rig into town and tells her that the rig broke down in Savannah, and he had to borrow money to get to town.

Those people that Charlotte work for on the island treat her real good. They care for Charlotte in a strange kind of way because Charlotte's momma worked for the old lady, and she would take Charlotte over to the island in the summertime when school was out. Charlotte went to some kind of school in one of the Carolinas, but she never went back after she come home for Christmas the first year. Well, nobody in the neighborhood said anything, and you know me, Janie, I mind my business. But you know, to this day I sure wish I knew what happened. Anyhow, like I was telling you, Elmore don't mean Charlotte no good. She should have been right here with us waiting for this bus. He either there with her now, or the poor fool waiting for him again.

Here comes the bus. He better have a good excuse for keeping us waiting this long.

Morning son, how you doing?

No, I don't have the right change. If I did, I been waiting so long my fingers too stiff to find it. You best take this here dollar and make the change.

You don't have change? That's okay, son. I know you is Bessie's boy. I'll just keep riding the bus each morning with you as the driver until my dollar runs out. What do you mean, you can't keep my money like that? It's my money, and I can let who ever I want hold my money. What do you mean you may not be driving this bus one morning?

Come on and get on this here bus, Janie. It's too cold to stand out there. No, Janie, I don't want you paying my fare. Look, son, you already thirty minutes late. No need to keep everybody else on the route freezing like I done got frozen. I'll just sit in my usual seat since you done got my money in your hand. By the time you get to my stop, you will just owe me seventy-five cents. Don't you

10

worry none, son, if you ain't the driver in the morning. I got sense. When Mrs. Arnold pays me for this day's work, I'll just ask her to give me a dollar worth of change, and I will have the change for the fare tomorrow if you are not the driver. Then, if you is the driver, I'll get on and take my usual seat, and you will only owe me fifty cents.

Son, ain't no need to argue. All these people done seen me give you my dollar. If you know you don't have no change, then why you take my money? I been real cold standing at this bus stop. It's real warm on this bus. Now, you can sit here all morning and burn up the gas on this bus, or you can start driving now. You know, son, I been doing some thinking. Since I suppose to be at Mrs. Arnold's house over forty-five minutes ago and I ain't there yet, I wonder how Mr. Arnold is gonna feel when I ain't there to keep them children for today only, while he and his lady go up state for the stockholders meeting for this here bus we is sitting on that ain't going nowhere. No, son, don't tell me to go there. Satan sure don't need me there when he got you.

Well, Janie, here is your stop. See you tomorrow.

Hello there, Mildred. Girl, you look all worn out, and the day is just beginning. So you going over to Mrs. Raymond today? You still calling her *Mrs. Four Days*? I remembers well the day you told me how when you first went there, and she asked how many children you have and if you got a man in your house. She was having that big ol' banquet at her house because her son had just got through with his doctor school. You cooked for days getting all that food together. A lot of food was ate, and lot of food was left. You told me how she kept that left over food in her box for four days and then told you to take it home to the children. Yeah, you took the food home alright. In fact, you found out that you would always be given the food four days after the big eating went on. Lord, I won-der what she would say if she knew that the garbage man probably wondered how you could afford to throw so much food away. But you know, Mildred, you used your head. Only thing you could have done was to tell ol' Mrs. Four Days thanks, and tell a whooping lie that the children really does enjoy the food she sends to them. Mildred, you listen to me now. You keep on doing what you have to do until you get some of them children through school. Then, with that done, maybe you can just work two or three days. You just look forward to the day when you can get on this here ol' late bus and tell all these ol' nosy bodies that your children is helping you, and you don't need to work hard no more.

·Look at Alice sitting back there so smug. Take her daughter, Sara Lee. She eighteen now and done finish high school. Tried getting a job in the department store, and they told her she could not be hired as a sales girl because she did not have any experience, but they did have an opening in the stockroom. Alice told me personally out of her own mouth that Sara Lee asked the manager how could she get experience if no one would hire her. Sara Lee went home and told Alice that everybody tells them to get a diploma so that they can get good jobs, but no one will hire them. They will soon have to have more than a high school diploma. Didn't do Sara Lee much good to get that piece of paper. Mind now, like I told you, I always mind my own business.

That's Sara Lee sitting back there in that green and white dress, behind her momma Alice. She riding this same bus just like we is. They tell me that Sara Lee come home one day 'bout three months ago from across the river where she working now, and went straight to her room crying and carrying on. They say that Sara Lee would not eat. Well, honey, Alice went into that room and made Sara Lee tell her what happen. Seems like Mr. Phillips made Sara Lee go to bed with him when Mrs. Phillips went to some kind of delegates women tea. Said Mr. Phillips told Sara Lee she better not stop working 'cause Mrs. Phillips knows that her kind of people only lie and steal. Sara Lee going to work over there still, dare not stop working. Mr. Phillips still doing what he want to do when Mrs. Phillips ain't home. She use to be skinny, but she had a good shape with what flesh she got. Noticing how she putting on some weight lately. Ain't' no use in Alice telling people Sara Lee secretly been married for five months. Folks on this here bus knows the difference. When Sara Lee told ol' Mrs. Nellie's girl, Gladys, that bad thing Mr. Phillips been doing, I knowed since then what been going on.

That girl back there in the yellow dress is Mary Ann. The folks she been working for, I hear tell, is from up north. Mary Ann swears that the lady treats her like one of the family. They goes to the grocery store together, and they shops together just like friends. She gets to ride in the front seat of the car. I says to myself, if riding in the front of the car puts her in the family, then she gets to eat at the table the same time; then, she better be prepared to sleep over in the house when that lady goes to the hospital to have that baby. I bet she gets the same money.

Funny thing happen to Flossie back there I bet she never forget. She worked for ol' lady Metz across the bridge. Kept my mouth shut when she told me how nice Mrs. Metz was to her, giving her food and clothes to take home. Come Friday, she get twelve dollars. When she ask old lady Metz if she would get the rest of the money next week. Mrs. Metz told her she been paying her help off for years in food and clothes. No need to give them more than twelve dollars a week when she been feeding and clothing them. Then, if this don't take the cake, ol' lady Metz tells Flossie to come in on Sunday because her daughter, Mrs. Harris, was coming in from down Savannah way, and since she had told Mrs. Harris about how good Flossie's chicken taste, Mrs. Harris sure wanted some. Flossie told me that she was thinking that there would be a cold day in Satan's flames when that there daughter of Mrs. Metz had any of her fried chicken. Flossie never did go back there. I laughs now when Flossie gets on this here bus.

See that other girl that just got on the bus? She got on a white uniform and white stockings. She is a real nurse. She ain't like some of them aides that puts on a white uniform and tell the people in the neighborhood they is nurses. She is a real nurse, alright. I remember when my sister Ellen was alive, and I was in her room at the hospital. This white nurse told her to hurry up and go to empty the bed pan. That there same girl told her loud, "I am a nurse and so are you. You go ahead and empty the bed pan." That white nurse turned red like a beet. I declare, it sure did me a lot of good to see that. She's nice, sure is nice. Just like one of us. Speaks every day. Sure was raised right. I can tell that right away. Tammy is her name. Sure sound pretty. *Tammy.*

Remember big Ada that got so sick last winter? That's her boy sitting up there by that there white lady. He don't have to sit in that there seat, but he say he just do it to make her draw up in the seat. He keeps doing it, and pretty soon she gonna stop riding this here bus. Been trying to tell Ada that equal rights is good, but ain't no need to ask for trouble. That same boy got on the bus last week telling about how Susie's daughter was at the bus stop, and this white man drives up and tells her to come and go with him. She said she told him yes, but to go home and get his sister and she will get her brother and they can double date together. Susie's daughter said he called her all kinds of names.

Carol told me that she is working for Mrs. Butler now on Tuesdays, and she said, "Lord do those folks carry on." Told me that Mrs. Butler must have headaches every time Mr. Butler comes home. She complains so much Mr. Butler done told her he best stay on the road 'cause she sure don't do him no good as a wife. Every time he come home, Carol says she has another bedroom to clean. Same thing happen to me when I been with

Mrs. Marshall. When Mr. Marshall home, a body would think I has one bedroom to clean, but that ain't so. I still has two bedrooms to clean. So, I says to myself, these white folks ain't getting along right. They sure ain't living like no husband and wife. Mind now, I was minding my business, but one morning at the breakfast table I hears Mr. Marshall tell Mrs. Marshall that he just the bread bringer, and all Mrs. Marshall want him to do is to keep her in a big house trying to keep up with her fool sister. Mrs. Marshall starts to yelling, telling Mr. Marshall that he hates her sister because her sister knows that he is one of them there sex perverts. Whatever that is.

Anyhow, Mr. Marshall tells Mrs. Marshall her sister should know. Mrs. Marshall screamed and called Mr. Marshall a nasty weakling. I goes back in the kitchen minding my own business, but I still hearing what they saying. Mr. Marshall call Mrs. Marshall a cold fish that hides behind headaches because she can't function like a normal wife. Sure wish I could have heard more, but Mrs. Marshall runs out of the room. But, honey, I sure ain't been ready to hear what I hear Mr. Marshall say. He yelled to Mrs. Marshall, "As for your sister, she may be a fool, but she sure is all woman." Then I hears him saying to himself, "Too bad I can't be married to a fool instead to a woman so damn cold like a piece of china." I declare, I left out of that kitchen. I went back to the laundry room and put the same clothes I just wash back into the washer. Mrs. Marshall sure had the cleanest wash in town that day. I been too glad to leave that house that day.

That Gladys Bradley that just got off the bus. She only irons these days. Tells me she sure is an ironer. Feel sorry for her though. That no good boy of hers is just lying around the house talking about his leg hurt. If he would stop eating so much and work, he would lose some of that fat and cause the weight not to be so much on his legs. Gladys gives him money to go to the clinic. That boy don't know what the clinic look like on the inside. Jake's Beer Parlor is his clinic.

We did have one good white driver one time to drive this bus for us, remember? I well remembers how that time the white lady complained about us sitting at the front of the bus. He told her, "Lady, driving this bus is my job, and I don't care where you or nobody else sit." Girl, I tell you, she looked at him and called him *white trash*. Some of the school boys tried to act up when he first started driving, but he put them in their places. I was glad to see that. Don't make no difference to me what color you is. You wrong, you wrong in my book. I lost my transfer one day. He told me, "That's alright, Miss, I remember you." Sure was surprised when he called me *Miss* and not *Auntie*. Can't figure out why he say he remembers me. One time, they always say we all looks alike. Seen one colored, seen 'em all.

Don't see Rosalie riding no more. She the one that worked for Mr. Harrleston. Been cleaning for that family for years. Mr. Harrleston never did remarry. Poor Mrs. Harrleston been bedridden for an awful long time. Poor soul just up and died one day. Rosa Lee was worried about Mr. Harrleston. He took it right bad. Rosa Lee was gonna get her boy, Samuel, to help Mr. Harrleston around the yard. They tell me Rosa Lee forget about that when she went back to the house one Friday to get some potatoes. She forget when Mr. Harrleston was suppose to be out of town. Honey, she walked into the house, and there was Mr. Harrleston all decked out in a lady dress, high heels, and a wig. Rosa Lee said she could have gone through the floor. So many things she could have done, but dare not say anything, she just got the hell out of there and ain't been back since.

White? No, honey, she ain't white. I knows her just like I knows my sister. We went to the same school. Sat in the same class. Had the same teachers. I finish the fourth grade, and she went through the seventh. Can't understand why she has to work so hard. She

16

colored alright. Black just like me and you. I can recall now when her sister went to New York and married that there white man. Come right back here living and spending money like water, and her poor sister doing day work in the same neighborhood. Been talking to her at prayer meeting on Wednesday night. She living by the grace of God, she say, and living the true life of who she really is. Still ain't talking about where that there husband is. Never miss a Sunday of church. 'Less she sick. That going to be one big funeral when she passes to her reward.

Hear tell Janie Mae done gone and joined that other church. The reverend and she sure don't set horses. Janie Mae say the reverend just a-shouting and telling her how she going to hell 'cause she drinks. Sure she drinks. Don't the reverend drink all the communion wine that left? My Bible tells me there is a time and a place for everything. I deem it ain't the place to be drunk on Sunday 'cause that His day. I does my drinking on Friday night and Saturday. When I goes to church, I am thankful to the Almighty for blessing me to be in His house, and as sure as hell, Reverend got no business talking about drinking. I does enough of it on Friday and Saturday night, and I sure as hell don't want to hear about it on no Sunday. Between you and me now, I sure can't fault Janie Mae much 'cause Reverend is a bitter pill to swallow at times. I getting along in years now, and I can't be going from church to church 'cause I don't like what the man is saying. When a body gets this age, it ought to have some kind of church roots.

My sister Frances is doing real well now. She went down to the place and talked to a lawyer. Them folks sure treat her nice. Get nice letters from them asking her to please come in at her convenience. Lordy, ain't that a turn around.

That's the new bank branch we just passed. Saw Doris' daughter working in there the other day. Sure makes a body feel good to see that. Of course now, that's the second one been in there. The other one was so light looking a body had to look awful hard to be sure she one of us. Told those people at the council meeting with the people from the bank that we wanted a face there so all of us will know we is represented. How come I know so much? I goes to the community meetings. Times is changed, honey. This ain't no time to sit at home.

Take Ethel over on Judy Street. She don't know the letter A if it's big as a house, yet she over at the school working in the cafeteria. Her sister is married to the principal. Sure wish I knew somebody. My sisters too dumb to marry bright men. My brother Albert, now he different. He married to a nurse. They got themselves a nice brick house. Gives Momma a little money every now and then. He working over at the ship yard. Hard work, too. Albert say a hard days work never hurt nobody. He been working long enough to know. His wife, she pretty nice, too. No pretending about her.

There is as much difference between Albert and my other brother John. I bet John got the first penny he ever made. I be so scared at hurricane season. I swear his old house will go at the first wind. Been telling him for years he best do something. Come telling me it been standing this long, can stand longer.

Patricia and her husband rode the bus last Friday. I thought they would do battle right then and there. From what I could hear, he called her filthy, and she asked him, if she was so filthy, why did he always bother her. He told her he was doing better. Sure is a shame they has to air their problems in the street. Now, the man ain't all wrong if you ever been to that house of theirs. From a child I always did hear the old ladies say that, when a house is not clean, people never look at the man. They always look at the lady in the house. He ain't said no lie now. He is doing better. But it ain't my business to say who he doing better with.

My oldest girl Elizabeth expecting her third baby now. Crying the blues to me about how she hate going to the community hospital. Telling me they always puts her on the table and leaves the door

18

open, and people passing by can look in on her. Talking about she must look like a big, black elephant lying up there. I tells her she best pretend she is an elephant 'cause all she got to pay is a drop in the bucket compared to what some people has to pay. She been an elephant twice before. The third time should be easy. Told her there ain't nothing wrong with her feet. Get up and close the damn door.

There's Edith Mae over there. Morning, Ella. How you doing? Knew I should not have asked her that. Think a body that young would not have so many things to complain about. Feels good before I ask. I seems to take on her misery after listening to her. Right out of school she been riding and complaining.

Where you say you working? Oh, yes! That where that new division is located across the creek. Went over there to pick up Sister Elnora with Sister Ruth last week for a meeting. Remember when the place was just a swamp. They done build it up and got some big homes over there. She *lives in* now. Never could stand live in jobs. Sister Elnora tells me her time ain't her own. Them little bitty children real crazy about her. They want to spend all their time with her. They cried and carried on when Sister Elnora left the house.

That there lady she works for is sure enough a lady. She from somewhere in the mid west. She was the president of the Island Creek Club, but they put her out. I hear tell from Azzie Mae that works for Mrs. Hall that the vice president of the Island Creek Club start saying that the lady was coming into the club with strange ideas. Say she start calling Elnora, *Miss Elnora*, just like Elnora her equal. Elnora say her lady tell them off, that she respects Elnora, and she will not let her children call Elnora by her name. They must call her *Miss Elnora*. She made it plain that Elnora can ride in the car up front, eat at the table when she takes her lunch any time she felt like doing so. Elnora told me out of her own mouth that she want to do more for her lady because she feel like she is not looked down on. Elnora told me that she was so mad with that Mrs. Hall because her lady come home from the club crying that they voted her out of office. They got some kind of crazy rule about impeaching, whatever that is.

Anyhow, Elnora say that her lady say she will not treat her housekeeper like dirt just because her skin is a different color. Elnora say she felt bad, but she did not let on how she was feeling. She just told her lady that this is the South. Some things just don't seem to change with some people. Elnora say she going to work there as long as she is able to work.

I never could figure it out. They eats our cooking; we tends their children. Still, some thinks we animals. I ain't saying all white folks like that. There is bad in all of us, but I declare, we always accepted them. They always could go into our places of business and enjoy themselves, but on the other hand, we is open to them and they is closed to us.

How you say your momma doing? Just trust in the good Lord, honey. She been lower than that, and the Lord smiled on her and she still with you. Take care of your momma, baby. Take care of her.

Dorothy Jenkins just got on the bus. It's almost her time. She goes to the hospital every week now. Hi there, Dorothy. Good to see you. Her oldest girl twenty-five now and got three children, and here Dorothy is expecting her eighth child. I declare, if it was me, I would be tearing up Patsy's back side now. Patsy is Dorothy's fifteen year old girl. That devil of a girl was stealing her momma birth control pills. The way I heard it was that Dorothy was not counting the pills, and when the pills ran out, she just thought she took them all. Anyhow, if this one be a girl, she can sure name it *Pillett*, and not *Paulette*. And that ain't all. Her girl Patsy looking to have a baby, too. I declare, you just don't know what is going to happen next. Dorothy can take care of another one, but she say it's just finding out that Patsy been laying and lying to her.

20

She broke down, and she been sickly ever since. I told her myself that maybe this baby she carrying now is the one that will help her and take care of her. You know, some folks just love children, and then again, some folks just can't stand children at all, but I'll tell you this, any child born to Dorothy Jenkins is a blessed child. Patsy still in school, but they good at the hospital. They make Patsy appointment for after school. Looks like the two of them gonna have them babies close at the same time.

You know riding this bus is like a good old church outing. You see so many people that you know. Anytime one is missing, I knows right away. Funny how we always sits in the same seat.

Hang on, honey. He can turn these corners as sharp as he want to. He don't bother me none. He the fool not to realize that, if we ain't on these here buses, he ain't gonna have no job. That's his fault he don't have no change. I is suppose to have money for the ride, and I done give it to him. Now, I finish with that.

I have to go over to Mrs. Blake this afternoon to help out a little bit. She is a lovely lady, but she is so frail, and she so scared of Mr. Blake. The only thing about going over there is I dislike the way Mr. Blake overlook little Hester. She is the baby, and she only three years old. She is the one that was born with the birthmark with white hair sticking out. It takes up most of the left side of her little face. Mr. Blake don't take up no time with her. Time comes when he just have to talk to her, and then, afterwards, he just locks up in his book room and drinks. Hester is a feeling child. She always wants me to hold her. I do because, I declare, I love her. She cry to play out with the other children, but they just keep her shut up. They say they don't want her to get hurt. But I know they keep her in because of that mark on her face.

Course now, I never say nothing to anybody 'cause it ain't my business, but I declare, I'll tell *you*. They show too much love for them other children of theirs. I believe that when a person hold children or anything first before the Almighty, He will take it away. That same little Hester going to be here for a long time because she sweet. She kind, and I believe that God smiling on her in a special way. Besides, they got doctors that know how to move things off the body.

Would you just look at that. I declare every time I pass by that there doctor office, people standing and waiting. When I on my way back from work, them same people sometimes outside waiting to see that doctor. It's a shame before the Lord how them people has to wait in all kinds of weather to see him. He still got the sign up there saying office hours until three o'clock. He ain't been in his office before three o'clock for years. Jake wife went there about a month ago, and she come telling me the reason why she put up with it 'cause he one of us. Shit, I don't care if he is one of us. The way I see it, my time is important too. I ask her why don't she go there at three o'clock, instead of going so early. She come telling me the nurse give her a ten o'clock appointment time. That nurse give everybody a ten o'clock appointment time, and the nurse herself don't get there until almost three o'clock. If that doctor had any sense, he would bring in a young doctor to work with him. This what I getting at, since he can't get in until late, let the young doctor go in at ten o'clock and stay until three o'clock and then he come on in hisself.

That what faults our people; his last child in college now, he got a big house and three cars, mind you. Now, he don't care nothing about his patients. I remembers well when he first move there to start doctoring. He use to be in all day long and well into the night. Now, he independent. He don't need nobody now, the same thing gonna happen to his family when he die that happen to that other doctor. Child, that doctor boy turn into a drunk, never did finish school, and he still going to one of them hospital for *recycle*.

22

Well if it ain't called *recycle* it call *re*-something. Anyhow, don't go getting smart on me. You know what I mean. It's a drunk hospital. That's what it is for sure. He just give them two children of his too much. They had cars in high school. Drove one of them BWM cars to college. Well, if it ain't a *BWM*, then it must be a *BMW*. Anyhow, you seem to know what I mean 'cause you sure as hell correcting me on everything I trying to tell you. Well, girl, here your stop. Sure hope you have a good one. See you later if I wanting to and the good Lord is willing.

Lordy Lord, have mercy. Look at Anna Bell sitting back yonder. I wonder at times why she wears them wigs so long, hanging and flying. She come back from Chicago and would not even give people the time of day. She ain't learned her lesson yet. Yeah, she the one got the wig snatched off. Elsie boy, Jack, tell all over at the grill that he snatch Anna Bell wig off when she sat by the window of this here bus. Well now, this don't have to be the exact bus, but it sure done happen on this cross town bus route. All them fellows ask him why he do a thing like that. He tell them she think she so high and mighty and pass all them on the street and don't even say a word. He say he got a lot of words from her that day. He wait good 'til the bus start to pull away from the stop, then he reach in the window and snatch the wig off. The bus run in one direction, and he off a-running in the other direction with all this hair in his hand. Hear tell Anna Bell come back home that day looking like a *banana lady*. Head all done up in a fancy wrap scarf.

She different from them sisters of her. They friendly girls. That one name Vera is one singing girl. Last year at the BTU meeting she set the church on fire singing. Honey, if I could lift my voice like that child, I would be on one of them records for sure.

Morning Beatrice. The big day almost here. Sure, I gonna be there. I can't miss the wedding. With all them bride maids coming in the church, this old arthritis neck better be straight to see your girl Hazel in that fine gown you done got her. You say the gown real lacy and white, too? Her two children in the wedding, I hear. Who care what people say. When them same talking people gives you the money for your girl wedding, then them same people can tell you your grands can't be in their momma wedding. All I can say is that your girl pregnant with she third child, but this time she gonna get the papers for this here baby that coming. It's a cross for sure, but you bearing up good, Beatrice. Hold your head high now. Don't you go forgetting what happen to Ellen's girl. Tell me she tried turning hers back. Got the infection and call the doctor. That the same girl lie that she had the stomach cramps.

I tell you what I know, honey. This don't come through other people to me. This come straight to me. That been about four years ago. Them stomach cramps calling Ellen *Grandmomma* these days. I tell Ellen then, no need to feel shame. That same little one might be the one to take care of her one day. From what I see, that other girl of hers too busy to even visit her. She live somewhere cross the river. Everybody knows when she comes to Ellen house. Sit in that there car and blows the horn like she crazy.

Who you working for now, Beatrice? Ain't that Doctor Powell daughter? Stop! What that you say? I bet they been too fit to be tired. Yeah, they may be the pillars of the community, but the pillars of their house done crash down. Divorce done touch many homes. Just 'cause he a doctor, he can't help it if a grown woman divorce. How come she don't know her husband be black? Honey, I been walking around this town and riding this bus a long time. I knows who white and who black. I knows who is passing for white, and I knows how to mind my business. Take Vivian that works for Mrs. Price. Her sister Nellie went north. She passing. She ain't look back this way no time. When the daddy pass, hear tell she had the flu and could not come. When the momma die, she had to have the operation. All them others come both times. I declare, God knows what he done when he made all them different colors. That been some funeral them two times. That family like a pretty flower garden, all colors in that family. Some been at the funeral whiter than her.

So what if she married to a white man, honey, this ain't no 1949. Course, they been doing it all the time up north and other places. We been having nighttime integration and daytime segregation ever since slavery. What we see just prove that what happen at night come to light. Honey, Doctor Powell daughter can get fifty of them divorces, but that ain't gonna take away the fact that her children half black. I just want to be around this ol' town when Doctor Powell find out he ain't all white. Do I know for sure? Is a blue bird blue? Don't matter none to me. We ain't crossing no more. We done criss cross. Music done change. People change. Use to say if you want to tell who passing, just plug in black music and watch to see who feet pat right to the beat of the music. Use to be a sure sign. They all hanging out together now. Never seen so much of jerking and jiving by all. Music done more than the churches do. Music bring people together. That is a sure good sign; if old people leave these young ones alone, all the hate will go away.

Look like the sun trying to come out. That is a good sign. Don't need no more rain. Streets flood too quick down here. Do I see? Sure I see what he doing. He can roll them eyes at me all he want. He got my dollar, and I riding this bus. He best watch where he driving. He wreck us real bad on this bus, and we might all own a car. No, I don't know how to drive. Never had to drive. Always had a bus to ride. Beatrice, your hearing ain't right. I say we might all own a car. I ain't said nothing about driving a car. Ha ha ha. I can see Mrs. Arnold eyes popping now when I roll up in a car. Guess I can put a sign on the side of the door saying *ironer for a day*. That should bring in a lot of business.

Excuse me. You talking to me, Anna Bell? Why sure, honey. I'll be glad to hand out these here cards of yours. Say, you done finish beauty school? Now, I declare. Ain't that something. Sure didn't know you been in school. That's one on me. You gonna open a shop? You gonna work with Opal? Hear tell that Opal got four girls and two fellows in there working. Wish you success, dear. When you gonna start working? Right now, today? Go on, girl. Stop! It's not? Sure, I remember hearing about what happen. I would swear its a wig. A weave you say? You say you specialize in weaving? All that hair hanging and flying must cost a lot of money. This here card say *consultation* by your name. What that mean? Now I know what you mean. Sure I know your sister Vera. Honey, Vera sing like an angel. Now, that girl got a angel voice and a heavy head of hair. She always look so pretty singing in the choir group. I like it better when she sing by herself. Them others try to out sing Vera, but they ain't got no stuff for her. They be searching for the note, and Vera done got the note and gone. Anna Bell, hush your mouth. That ain't Vera's hair? You mean to tell me you put that in Vera hair ever since you been back from Chicago? So, you decided to stop wearing the wigs when Elsie boy snatch your wig. How you put all that in on your own head? Opal did that? Now, I see. You teach Opal, and you and Opal gonna clean up weaving this hair. Hope you don't mind me saying, but I sure like Vera hair. Sure honey, I know you got to wear it long to advertise your business.

Go right ahead and ask your question. Sure, I act surprise when you got up from back yonder and sit here to talk to me. You never done this before. No, honey. Nobody never tell me why you come back from Chicago. Jail? You don't need to tell me no more. That all your business. Take it from me. Leave it all in Chicago. You heading in the right direction now. You got your beauty license, and you ain't in your momma house bootlegging. You too smart to be a kitchen beautician. You a license beautician now, and you gonna be doing legal work. Something tell me you gonna do real good in Opal shop. I been going to the same shop over twenty years, and they still nice to me over there. If you had just give me these cards and tell me to pass them out and not take the time of day to sit and talk, honey, these cards would go in this old brown pocketbook here with a fix smile and out in Mrs. Arnold trash can with a frown.

Tell you what I gonna do. My church got a lot of young ones in the young adult choir. I gonna see that these cards go to them. Then, I tell them to look at Vera hair. You think Vera gonna mind me telling that ain't her hair. Ha ha ha. So, Vera gonna tell them it her hair 'cause she done buy it. Got that right.

Hope you don't mind me saying so, Anna Bell, when you board this here bus, you needs to smile and say hello to everybody on here. Even to that ol' fool bus driver who keeps rolling his eyes at me. Honey, personality important in this world, specially your business. They might not talk back right away, but you keep on doing it. They gonna break down and talk. At first they gonna be surprise just like me. They got no way of knowing how you hurting inside. And don't you go telling them about what happen in Chicago. You look real nice. Hear tell Opal got a real classy shop. No flip shoes worn in there. 'Bout time one of our shops come into being. Your stop next. Sure, I'll see you tomorrow. I mean to talk loud so everybody on this bus hears me. Just let him try to stop me from sitting on this here bus tomorrow. When I get through with him, and if he recover, he will learn about the skeletons in my closet and why I am a born again Christian. Them others made a mistake by pushing me. He be just another fool. Don't nobody stop me from going to my church and work. I work to pay my tithe to my church, and my God and church keeps me strong to go to work. I keep the faith, and he best damn well keep his seat.

Hello there, Miss Milton. That is one pretty collar you got on. Sure, I remember your grandmother. God done bless her. Her eyes still good to see how to make them pretty stitches of lace like that. She always did dress you up real pretty. I always say how proud we is of you. You a good example of how where you grow up don't keep you from doing good in school. I can tell you a special kind of teacher. The school system really need more teachers like you. Our children needs a role model like you. You knows how they be hurting 'cause you right at the center and can tell what going on. But tell you the truth Miss Milton, we needs parents like your grandmother Mrs. Williams. Teachers can't do it alone. We needs to get the mommas and the daddies to be parents. If there ain't no daddy in the house, then momma got to demand respect. Things so bad now, momma nor daddy getting respect from they own children. Then, they wants the teachers to handle children like that.

Come up after Sunday school a few Sundays ago. I tell the children that when I was growing up, if a neighbor saw me doing something wrong, the neighbor spank me, took me home, and daddy spank me too. Well, you try that now. You spank the child, the neighbor beat you up and sue you, too. Ha ha ha. I laughing now because, one day coming home from school, I pass Miss Flossie house and say good evening and kept on marching on home. Mind now, Miss Flossie sister, Miss Rose, and the brother, Mr. Phillip, was all sitting on the porch. Well, Momma met me at the door and spanked me for not speaking. I kept crying and swearing to Momma that I did speak. Daddy was feeding the chickens in the back yard, and he heard me crying. I would have gotten away with a spanking from only Momma, but my loud crying really got Daddy in on it. Well, Miss Milton, he spanked me because I did not say *good evening, Miss Flossie, good evening, Miss Rose*, and *good evening, Mr. Phillip*. He taught us to respect older people by calling them by name. Tell that to these children now, and they think you crazy.

I know you teachers works real hard. I voted for the tax increase some time ago. Did it because they say it was needed to give teachers a raise. From what I hear tell teachers going through these days, money might not keep them in the classroom. Parents better start helping out more with their own children.

You know something, Miss Milton. It might not be too bad an idea to start teaching the lessons by music. Lord knows all of these children know the words to every record they hear. I believe that, if they can sing the words to the records, they should be able to sing the words to the lesson records. Maybe somebody gonna come up with the idea. Course now, they might just say it take too much money for that. It ain't never too much money for a new football field.

That's another thing that gets on my nerves. Them old, no good daddies don't do nothing for them children when they growing up, and just as soon as they get into the games big time, here they come around talking about *my* son or *my* daughter. I feel real good when I see them on television and they says *hi Mom*. That tells the whole world it be the momma who stood by that child. Sometimes the daddies do right. I just wish somebody would come up with the idea to get the record of every child that has really done something good that went to these schools in this city and went on to do good. What we hear mostly on the news and see in the papers is what bad they done got into. Every two or four years they should put in a big spread and print up how successful these children are. Now, that should give the younger ones something as a role model to look up to. I don't care if they collect trash. That is a job. They ain't stealing, and somebody got to do it. They needs to be taught that all work is honorable if it is honest work.

Sure enjoy talking to you today. You too, Miss Milton. Have a good day. Be sure to tell your grandmother Mrs. Williams hello for me. Sure, she will remember me. God bless you. Keep up the good work.

Come sit here by me, Catherine. Here comes Romona. I sure don't feel like hearing about no grandchildren this morning. She got baby pictures like some folks got credit cards. Flip from one to the other, and they all gonna give her hell. It gonna take them children all year to spell in school when they starts just to learn how to spell them names their momma done laid on them. Talking 'bout they African names, and they need to identify with *Mother Africa*. Well, her children don't know what Africa like, and never stayed in school long enough to find it on a map. Catherine, them children don't know nothing 'bout no Africa. It gonna take the teachers half a year to say them names right, and the rest of the year to practice to squeeze the names on the roll book. Sure, I know they using them computers in school now for reports. I ain't dumb. I still say computer gonna put out what man or woman put in.

Don't ask me. I don't know why that girl name them children them names. But, I can tell you this, each one sure as hell got a nickname, 'cause Ramona can't even say them names herself. Such pretty little girls they is. I feel sorry for them, though. Why? 'Cause they ain't gonna have no hair around they hair line. Honey, them braids is too tight. Every time I see them little sweet girls, I can swear that the hairline done gone back. Who, me say something? Honey, you must be crazy. You know I minds my business. Sure, you can tell easy by looking. When you see them little white bumps at the scalp and the hair pulling, why that be the sign of trouble. She had one little girl when she been little, she always had droopy eyes. Damn if she ain't got slant eyes from them tight braids. Don't know why they put in them braids so tight. Do I like them? Now, I seen some pretty ones, and whoever fashion them things on them heads I seen them on sure knows what they been doing. They looked right pretty to me. They ain't too tight when the ones putting them in knows what they is doing. Sure, they can cost a lot of money, but, honey, I knows some girls in the city can really do their stuff when it comes to them braids. Don't need no license for that. The beautician's doing it and charging a lot of money for it, too. Them young girls doing it for a little of nothing, and people going to them, too.

Catherine, what is this I hear about Romona son Randolph being a doctor? Is you a nurse? Then, how the devil he gets to be a doctor? I know he been at that hospital for a long time, but he ain't no doctor. Who told me? You don't have to know that, but just as sure as you and me sitting here on this bus, he ain't no doctor. When he was doing his time in the pen, he was doing orderly work in the hospital up there. They put him on that pre-release deal thing they got now, and he been at the hospital upstate working. He been right there until he got the full parole. I know for a fact he can't leave from that town, unless he tell the parole officer he got to report to. She lying, just like she lying that she own that house they all living in. She paying a house note just like you. No I ain't paying no house note. Why? 'Cause Momma done turn over the house deed to me. She done tell all the others I be the one really taking care of her, and them others just throw a little change on her from time to time. Well, I guess sometimes it is different when the boys is married and they got them wives to please. Anyhow, we doing fine, and ain't a soul squawking about what Momma done.

But, girl, you see how they fix up Ethel house? Praise the Lord! Them workers swept in there one day and start tearing down, digging and hauling away. Ethel never said a word to nobody. Honey, she held her peace. I was told that when Ethel heard that Peter was dead, she marched to that federal building, slap the license down on the man at the desk, then went back later with the original death certificate. Ain't been no copy either. It been the real thing. That just goes to show you. Ethel held on until her changes come. She let that woman up the road take care of everything. Honey, listen to me. I is telling you now. The fool paid for the funeral. That ain't all. She had four white family cars. Look it don't matter who was in the cars. None of Ethel children been in them. Them children went in they own cars.

Ethel got the insurance money and the social security checks. Divorce? What Peter know about a court divorce. That woman been thinking all she got to do is live with Peter. Ethel well and alive. That woman the fool for not making sure there ain't no legal wife. In life, all Peter done was give Ethel five children and a damn hard time. No, he ain't had none by that other woman. He been burn out by then, I guess. She ain't that young. She on the dark side of sixty for sure now. All them years he been at the yard sure done paid off for Ethel. She done add two bedroom and a den. Getting a car, too. She sure enough come into a lot of money.

Ethel a good momma to them children. She never paint no bad picture about Peter to them children. She figure they were gonna find out 'bout the daddy themself. They done it, too. They never ask him for nothing, and they been doing all they can for Ethel. That sad looking house even look happy now. Told me why she brick it in. No, she don't worry 'bout painting no more. Yep, they all went to the funeral. Ethel say they Peter children, and she sure was not gonna say anything against their daddy when he dead, 'cause she held her peace while he been living. Still, can't figure out how she got the death certificate so fast. Anyhow, the children seen him in the grave. Honey, he planted way out in the country. I say they all went to the funeral, not Ethel. She had a big dinner cooked for them when they come back from the country.

32

Hi, Griffin. Now that is one clean looking man. He always looks good and starched. His clothes may be stained, but they clean stained, washed and ironed. I ain't never seen him in wrinkle clothes. He be a proud man, too. Married? Not that I knows. Took care of his momma until she died. All the young girl call him a *l.b.d.* Tell me that mean he a *loving bedroom dude*. He got a lot to offer somebody.

Hey, Rachel. Sit on down here, girl. I know what you mean. These tracks bad enough as it is. Don't pay his driving no mind. He hot under the collar at me. Anybody holding their water gonna be in trouble, not me. That the last thing I does before going anywhere. He the one acting like a fool. Before he loosen me from this seat, this ol' body might shake like jelly, but my tail jamming in this here seat.

Frances sit by me in church the other Sunday. Almost cost me to fall to the floor. No, she done move off the project. She been staying in that project over thirty one years. Where she going after all these years? New York. Everybody I know trying to come down from up there. Them old bones of hers can't take them cold days up there. It's the check that what 'cause it all. You mean you ain't heard? Don't you remember when her oldest boy went to join the Navy a long time ago? He come back home to visit about four or five times. He ain't been back since, and he can't come back now. 'Cause he done died, that's why. Don't ask me, I don't know for sure. But I hear tell he got killed in some strange way, and some kind of civil legal lawyer take a big important company to court. His name was Charles. That's right. Charles been his name.

Anyhow, this Charles never been married. It been him and some more people dead at the same time. Since Charles ain't married, Frances, his momma, the next to kin. The check drop on Frances. Now, that ol' no good baby boy of her done sweet talk her into moving to New York. I just got a feeling that I ain't gonna see Frances no more. We been good friends for all these years. Now, you take me, if I had money like that, the first thing I would do is move out of the city. When it high tide, my street like the river. Many is the times I wade to get to this here bus.

Lewis, don't tell me you riding the bus these days. Man, it been a long time since I seen you. Sure, I still living. Well, now it true. I living the song now. I don't get around much anymore. People do change, and I ain't up to making no fool of myself. I good times right in my own house. Besides, I don't have no worrying 'bout nobody talking 'bout how much I drink and who I drinking with. Boy, we sure use to cut a rug. Don't believe nobody love dancing like you and me. Ha ha ha. Just look at us now. You got bunions so big you can barely walk, and me shaking like a jelly roll on arthritic knees. One thing for sure, the things we use to do we sure can't do no more. To tell you the truth, Lewis, sure don't think I would want to do like we use to in times like these. Too much shooting and mugging going on. Many times after dancing, I leave the hall walking, not a soul worry me. We bump and grind all over the floor, everybody happy. Hear tell a soul can't even brush up against you now. We made good of the sixty minute record when it come along. We hear every word, too. These records now, can't tell a thing they saying.

Shucks, Lewis, who you trying to fool? Took you almost five minutes to board this bus. I bet your heart muscles look like them bunions of yours. How often you be at the Veterans Hospital? They treating you alright over there? I don't know 'bout them others, but I know you deserves all the benefits you can get. Still catching hell, too, I bet. Let me see now. It been almost three years since I seen Hazel. She need to settle down. Four times it been. Four times Hazel marry a service man. She got her own United Nation. Got children with everyone she tied up with. No, Lewis. No divorce. She bury every one of them husbands. They was all legal 'cause she got full benefits from every one. I went to two of the funerals. We been friends a long time. Just could not bear to see her go through that two more times. I just stay at the two different houses and watch out while they all at the funeral each time. I use to call her. Every time I call her, she gets to complaining. I done told her that she got more than many we know. She luck out with four husbands. I had one jackass, that enough for me. No need for you to laugh, Lewis, you been just a good dancer. Notice nobody never take you home to a momma. You sure ain't gonna get taken now. Ha ha ha.

Hi, Evalina. Girl, you of all people. How come you miss Vivian wedding? Everybody at the reception sitting around like it be a wake. I been to some wakes with more life than that. Honey, Vivian took to the floor, tell the man playing the records something, and the next thing I know a solid two hundred and fifty pounds Vivian on the floor telling everybody this is a wedding reception, let's get it on. The wedding party got up and form a line, people got in line and everybody jump on the floor doing some kind of dance call the *electric slide*. Girl, when Vivian throw her big butt around, dipping and sliding back and forth, guess who hit the floor. Girl, I find myself on the line dipping and sliding all over the place. I ain't had so much fun in ages. Good thing the wedding been on a Saturday 'cause I let it roll, honey. The bottles started flowing, and I declare, I started feeling real good.

Charlotte was there. She on one end of the line, and that ol' fool Elmore standing by the bar with his ol' sourpuss looking self. I don't know why she have to drag him out. He don't know how to get down and have fun. Age don't have a thing to do with having fun. It all in the mind. Think old, you be old. Receptions are for celebrating. We all glad Vivian got married. She deserves happiness. Worked like hell to help send them sisters and brothers to school. Arthur was there too. He the baby boy. No, he ain't worth a pot to piss in. No damn good, if you ask me. The old family house fall on him when the others left. He let the porch floor and steps rot. I hear tell that the roof is sinking in now. High time Vivian do for herself.

Arthur telling everybody he a chef. He making hamburgers, that what he doing. I see him do that my own self. Don't know why he want to lie 'bout a job. He swear he sharp. Got a street name, too. Hear tell up the road yonder they call him *Ghetto Man*. Spend every dime he make playing the big shot. These girls downtown don't pay him no never mind. They know he ain't from what the horses do on the straw. Fat? That was the prettiest two hundred and fifty pounds I ever seen in a wedding dress. That girl been so good to her momma and daddy before they pass on, and we all knows it, too. Then, putting herself on the back burner to take care of the children. She could wear a sack at her wedding and still look pretty. People just love her.

Evalina, I ain't never seen that many people to a wedding and reception before. What you mean that if so many people been there, how come I know you ain't been there? Your mouth just like a bell clapper. As soon as you got on this bus and seen me, you was gonna start telling me 'bout the wedding and what you got from the mall store to wear. You always stressing yourself out trying to out dress everybody. Listen, Evalina, ain't we been friends near to forty-five years? How you think I feel when you always talking 'bout how much you pay for them clothes from the mall stores, and playing bingo and borrowing money from me and everybody else we know. I don't give a shit if you gets mad. I is your friend. That the reason I talking to you now. Them other folks grin in your face and talk behind your back. I minds my business. I always up front with people.

Then, another thing I notice 'bout you. You done hit 'bout every beautician in town. They done put a name on you, honey.

They all calling you *Be Right Back Evalina*. You sure as hell knows what I is talking 'bout. Oh, come on now, Evalina. You and me been getting our hair done two weeks ago, and you whisper and tell Sally you gonna go and get your check cash and be right back. You ain't been back yet. You good for that lie. What shop you gonna hit this week? That why you getting bald like a eagle. Too many hands in your hair. You better stick to one beautician.

No need to get mad at me. These young people in the shops ain't gonna let you get away with that mess you been pulling down. You might be getting old and gray, but you gonna be old, bald, and beaten if you don't stop that mess. You ain't changed from the time we been in school, and you tell Mrs. Benson at the store that you left your money at home, and if she give you the oranges you would be right back with the money. You need to change your ways. I bet you ain't going to them beauticians in the mall shop, sit in the chair, and when they done spend all that time on you, you gets up and talking 'bout you got to go and cash your check and you'll be right back. They call the police on you for sure. You probably stay home from the wedding 'cause, when you try to get your hair fix, every shop you call say they all book up. Still wearing the perm, too. I saw Sally rolling and setting your hair. You needed the touch up then, and you been broke. I ain't never known you to wear bangs. I see them teeth marks from the straightening comb on your forehead. No need to hide 'em from me. You been pressing them edges.

Where you going to bingo tonight? Hope you have some luck. Look out! Watch your step getting off this bus. The driver stopping on a dime this morning.

Lewis, you seen Margie lately? You ain't gonna see her on this bus no more. She the rich lady now. You mean you ain't heard? She the one that win that big lottery last April. Margie did not even want to go to Florida. If you can remember, she use to work on Miami Beach for years with a very rich family. She took care of the old lady, and when she die, Margie come back here. Told me she had enough of Florida. But then her girl Nell wanted her with her when she took the children to Disney. Margie say everybody in this place putting numbers on slips, and she just looking at little store things. Then Nell tell her to take a chance. She started not to 'cause that be gambling. Anyhow, she do up a slip, and she don't even know which numbers she black out. She put the tickets in her change purse and really forgot about them. Lord, lo and behold, the TV show the winning numbers in the motel room. She ain't been paying attention to no numbers. Nell write the numbers down and tell Margie they gonna check the numbers later. Honey, Margie walking round a rich woman at Disney, and don't even know it. Do you know Margie could have lost them tickets 'cause she been putting in and taking out change all day at Disney. They was no more thinking 'bout them tickets then. They all the way in Georgia at the rest stop when she mention the tickets. Lewis, Margie say, when they match up her tickets and one had the six numbers, everybody had to go to the toilet. Then, Margie say, everybody got happy, then they get real scared, like everybody at the stop know they got a money ticket. She say they got their behinds in the car so fast and made their way back home like a bat out of hell.

They so crazy, they call Margie lawyer that done the closing on the house when she move back from Miami Beach and ask him what to do. They had to go back to Florida, and they done put a lot of money down to Margie. She getting a lot of money every year for twenty years. She still pretty nice, though. Ain't no changes there. I here tell she buy a nice big house for Nell and the children. Who? Nell husband? He a nice fellow. He work longshoreman. He driving one of them Bronco trucks. He always been providing for his little family. He is a good, country fellow. I really like him. Nell had me over for the Fourth of July. Told me she wanted all of her momma friends over there together. Lewis, you would have been there, too, but nobody hardly see you no more. I still surprise to see you now. Margie gonna be some happy when I tell her you still on the side of the living, even if it is just barely living. Ha ha ha.

Wait, Lewis, let that fool driver stop full fore you try to get up. Hope you don't have to spend all day at the hospital. Good to see you, man. You take care now.

Rachel, you see that Lewis? He was one good timing man. We had us some fun times together. Funny though, when we is young, we never think 'bout what lies ahead. A lot of clean fun then. Never hurt nobody. Not like today. No drugs for us. Maybe a few beers, a little bit of shine, and, oh yeah, the gin. Gin was the thing. We had a little joke going that say, "It ain't no sin to drink gin." Somebody must a put something in the punch at Vivian reception 'cause I remember drinking quite a bit. I just had me a good weekend.

Why hello, Estell. Girl, you look good for days. Things looking up, eh? On your way to the eye clinic? Those glasses really look good on you. I been so use to seeing you in dark shades. You been wearing them dark shades long before you lose your sight. Almost five years, right? You sure got a lot to be thankful to God for. Not many people been blind and now can see. How the children and grands doing? They sure don't stay little long. Makes a body feel old for sure. You got some pretty, little, well behave ones. Not like some people, bringing the children to church, and the children shouting and making more noise than the minister.

I ain't being nosy now, but how Samuel doing? Back in Mississippi you say. Went back by his self? You mean the same woman, the secretary from the school? That woman had too much damn nerve. All them times she been coming to your

house pretending she there to talk 'bout the children and carrying on with Samuel all the time. Estell, how come you never tell
Samuel you started to see a little bit? Girl, I too glad you seen
what you done see. She standing in your house talking 'bout
your children and feeling and playing up to Samuel at the same
time. I bet ten devils come over you. Let me get this straight
now from you. I ain't too clear on exactly what happen. I ain't
one to believe what people talk. That keeps me from minding
people business. Just 'cause I hear things, that ain't no cause to
take it for gospel truth.

Okay now, so that woman standing in your living room talking
to you. All the time you ain't really blind at all, and you seeing
everything. Dear Jesus. Samuel holding her, and she squeezing all
over him, and she steady talking to you and squeezing Samuel,
too. Lord have mercy. I know what the end been at the emergency room at the hospital. Tell me what you did after you seeing
all that. So, you pretend to feel your way to the kitchen. The two
of them following you and doing up on each other. You goes to
the stove where you is cooking the collard greens. You say they
been the greens for the church social? People always did say you
cook good greens. I particular 'bout eating folks collards. Them
that see, I don't eat greens from. I don't mean no harm now, but
with you being blind, at least everybody thinking you is, I ain't
eating your greens. That's just me now. Anything else you fix
good to go, but no greens. I know you use the children to help
you, but them young children ain't careful in the picking like I is.

Now then, them two standing and kissing and not paying you no
attention. You pour the big roaster pot of collard greens all over the
two of them. I hear tell the woman had on one of them t-strap sun
dress. She run out screaming, Samuel rubbing his eyes and can't see,
then you picks up the pot of okra soup and throw it down the front
of Samuel. He screaming and wiggling on the floor. You walk

40

around Samuel, go to the minister house, and tell the minister a miracle done happen, you can see. Lord, now ain't that something.

It was the police man riding on the horse run down the woman and catch her. She done tore the top off that dress, and people say she had greens over her chest like Eve had the leaf over her in the garden. And them neighbors' children, they all running after the police on the horse, laughing and yelling. She been burn real bad, too.

What 'bout Samuel? Did he lose it? You knows what I mean. He still got it? Paul, the orderly at the emergency room, say Samuel cry like a baby, pleading with the doctors not to cut it off. He keep saying over and over again, "Fix it, doctor. For God's sake, fix it." Say Samuel hold hisself so tight, thinking the doctor gonna cut it off. Say Samuel a sight to see. Eyes closed with greens dripping from he head to the feet, and he there holding his private part crying, "Fix it, doctor." The okra slimy and slick, Samuel pulling that thing one way, and it shrinking and slipping out his hand. The doctor grabbing the thing, and it slipping out the doctor hand. Paul say they get Samuel to sleep when they put the needle to him. Say that was some mess to clean up. Samuel been in the burn unit for quite a spell. That woman been there, too.

You know, this here a big world to be so small. Who would think that Johnnie Mae be living in that town there in Mississippi where Samuel and that woman is now. Johnnie Mae write and tell her sister Jackie that Samuel come home and tell everybody he and the woman is married and that they got burned in a car accident. I tell Johnnie Mae she best tell Jackie to mind her own business in Mississippi. Them some mean people down there, and she sure ain't home. That be Samuel home, if he say he and that woman is married. They *is* married? If he say they done got burned in a car accident, all Jackie better say is car accidents can really be bad and put a period there. Life goes on.

But, Estell, how you get out of that? Samuel and that woman sure ain't been two to talk, and you at Reverend house with a miracle to see. No charges brought against you by them two. I guess they been shock more ways than one. The good book ain't never lied and never will. You sure wait for your changes to come. The Lord meant for you to see what you seen, but the devil made you do what you did.

No, now, I ain't saying you right nor you wrong, I don't pass judgement on nobody. Samuel best be glad you been the wife. Some of these girls riding this bus right now, if one of them been the wife, it would have been one of them *Frankie and Johnny* song shooting. You still pretty in eye glasses. I too glad you looking up. Take care of yourself. Don't look back. Put them eyes ahead of you. You gonna see, honey. Something out there good for you. You already did? What that be? Your divorce papers. No need to ask for more than that. Well, this your stop. Good thing you on this bus; you in plenty of time for your clinic appointment. Have some good news for me the next time I see you now.

Morning, Mae. Hear from your sister Sadie lately? Well now, you be in her shoes, you may as well do the same thing. How you gonna know what going on in your house when you leave 5:30 in the morning? For all she know, them girls been leaving the same time, going to school. All I can say is you takes a chance bringing in a man when you gots young girls in a house.

Where that man come from anyhow? Alabama? How she know that for sure? She been in touch with the family down there? The storm done blow in some saints and mostly devils, and it be just her luck to take up with the devil. Sure, Mae, I know you try to set her straight. You ain't been by yourself. He loafing round all day, and she busting her butt working all them long hours at the plant, and he messing up them girls at the same time. How much more time she got to spend? And you say she still ain't telling nobody what gone on? And them two niece of yours, they ain't said nothing to nobody. They still with your brother Lawrence in Ohio? How come I know that? Now, look here, Mae, ain't no cause for you to take that tone of voice with me. When I was told—and I ain't saying who done told me 'bout Ohio—I wants you to know that being the Christian I is, I have yet to say a word to another soul 'cause it ain't my business in the first place, and I always minds my own business.

Sadie mean for he to be dead. Hear tell she put all the gun bullets in that man and stab him, too. There you go again, asking me who done told me all that. It done happen over three years back, and you ain't tell me yet what they done with that man body. No, that ain't gonna work 'cause you just today tell me that man been from Alabama. It gonna be hard on Sadie 'cause she gots to live with that there killing all her days left in the pen or on the street. She done lost everything, and excuse me, but you and them others ain't done nothing to try to keep the house. The way I see it, Mae, you been on the project near to fifteen years, and it be better for you to move into Sadie house, that way you helps your sister and you has a better place to live in.

Listen, Mae, I know lots of folks that been living in the projects, and ain't nothing wrong with none of them folks. Some gonna get out, and for some, only the death angel gonna get 'em out. I here to tell you ain't no reason to give up. You crazy, talking like that. How you know ain't nobody been kill in the project house where you at now? You ain't getting no younger, and you going round telling everybody your boy Harold gonna buy you a house. How old Harold now? Thirty-five? How come he ain't married yet? So, he gonna wait 'til he pay for the car? I thought sure I see Harold the other day in a red car. But, Mae, you say Harold say he gonna buy you a house over six years back when he pay for the other car he been driving. He best hurry up and do something

43

'cause, if he gonna buy you that house and keep paying for all them new cars, time running out for somebody for sure.

Who been in the car with Harold? The same fellow who always be in the car with Harold, that who. No, I ain't got no attitude. You ask me, and I telling you it be the same man I always see with Harold, walking or riding. You ain't gots to explain nothing to me 'bout Harold friends. Sure fellows have fellow friends, but some fellows they got the girl friends, too.

Anyhow, I been asking you 'bout Sadie. When you go to visit Sadie, you be sure to tell her I say *hello*. You be sure now to do that for me.

Who you gonna work for today? Mrs. Bronsky? What store they own? The outlet store on Creek Road? No, I ain't been out there as yet. She a nice lady? Every time I look round this route riding this here bus, another store board up and close down. How they expect poor people to shop? Everything moving cross the bridge or up the road. I don't like it one bit. Bus fare going up and having to wait over half a hour for the bus ride one way, it just ain't right. Hear tell they suppose to put some shelter at these here bus stops. Sure hope they gets round to it. So cold this morning, shelter sure not much good if we had it already.

Mae, you ain't been riding this bus nowheres near the years I been riding. Sometimes, I says to myself I don't know how much longer I gonna be able to drag up on these here cold mornings. Then, I thinks 'bout how good the Lord been to me. I know the Lord gonna make a way for me one day. I been smart in paying the social security, and if the Lord bless me with a few more years, I gonna put some of these work days aside for me.

Well, your stop next one up. Mae, remember what I telling you now. Sadie a good momma; it ain't her fault what done happen, and you nor me know what we do if we walk in and find what Sadie find. One thing for sure, she done put that man where he ain't gonna hurt no more girls. Watch your step getting up. We is got a jackass for the driver today.

That be Vermell and Vernell getting on. They twins. Morning, girls. Ain't they pretty? Sure, they momma and daddy is teachers. Every Christmas holiday, they comes home from the college up yonder and works at the same store where they works in the summer when they is home. That what I been just trying to tell Mae. Them girls momma and daddy grow up on the project. They, too, been some smart children. Now, you take the daddy; he been smart two ways. He play ball and study the book. Playing ball put him right on through the teacher college, and now he be the coach and the teacher. The momma ain't been no fool now. That girl make a sewing machine jump for joy. Sew her way right on through school. She the one make all the choir robes that be so pretty for nearly all the churches. She teaching cooking and sewing at the high school.

Them children had good parents that give 'em a good environment. They grow up in the Sunday school and marry right out the church. No, not right away. They must have work for 'bout two years fore they get married. Next thing I know, the furniture store truck bringing all this new furniture to the project, and it be they house that gets the stuff. They live in that place close to ten years. Had them same twins there and two boys. The twins, they the first to come. Then, they had one of the boys, but something wrong with that one. He one of what you call a special child. The other boy, he be just fine. The twins play music, too. Vernell sing, but I hear tell Vermell say Vernell too good for her. She best bet is on the piano.

Now, what I really likes 'bout the momma and the daddy, they send them children right to the public school. Folks on the project betting they gonna send 'em to one of them there private schools. The momma and the daddy tell 'em that if the public school good enough for they to teach in and other folks send they children there, then they own children don't be no better. Them two girls march out of that school with high marks, too. They been number one and number two. No, not now; I did not say that. The momma and the daddy ain't teaching at the same school, and the girls ain't been in none of the school they teaching at. They finish from the new school when they separate the school. They call it some kind of *zoning*. All I know that after almost sixty years some people in high power say they got to zone, and next thing we all know, we gets another school. Now, we gonna see how long that last.

Sure they grandmomma and granddaddy still living. They still on the project. Where they going? Everybody know them, and they church standing right round the corner. Sure, they got drugs in the projects. They got 'em in the rich sections, too. Drugs all over. It ain't *where* you live; it be *who* coming to where you living. If you ask me, some might be riding this bus right now. The way that fool ass bus driver acting, how we know he ain't on something? It be the chance we take.

Them twins from a good family. Come time when the momma and daddy buy the house out the city, people cry like they move oversea. They check on the old people often. Ain't like some children I know, come every now and then and stay in the big car blowing the horn like they is crazy. They too busy to get out and sit a spell with the old folks. Some Fridays you should see them coming with all the little ones, with the plastic bags of clothes for the weekend. Use to be brown paper bags, even for them moochers it be the plastic bags. Never happen in my house. Sure, I loves my ones. I done work all week, I needs my time for me. My place is for me to stretch out in. Who I stretching with? Best be sure it ain't a soul you know.

You know, Agnes, I been thinking 'bout all them children that done grow up on the projects. Some done bad, and some done good. We never see nothing 'bout the good doings in the papers. A lot of them same children is now lawyers, doctors, nurses, and teachers, and I hear tell Ms. Bradley boy, Ernest, into drawing for contractors to build—I forget what you call it—but I hear tell he sure doing real good.

Then, look at all them children gone to the service. Lots of them sending money back home to help they momma with the little ones. Sure would be a good thing if they was to put some pictures of them children doing good in the papers. Now that be a good thing for the young ones to look up to.

Agnes, I been looking at you, and I been trying to figure out what so different 'bout you. You best stop putting them sponge rollers on your head. You getting clean round them edges. I ain't never seen you without them things on your head. When you take 'em out? Since when? The only difference now, you done change from the pink ones to the black ones. I know that head ain't feeling no kind of cold this morning. You got rollers on the head, a scarf, and the hat. You needs to let your head catch some air. Nerves? Honey, everything gone wrong with the body these days folks wants want to put it to the nerves. How them feet of yours doing these days? Still hurting at times? Course, now you never take hardly no time off after the big operation. Sure, I well understand your needs. People just don't understand when you gots to work, you gots to work.

You good, Agnes, a real hard worker. Many days I feel for you, seeing how you drag on them crutches and limping with the stick, catching this ol' bus, trying to make another day. It be a shame you done been put to this. Now, listen close to what I gonna say 'cause I say this directly to you, Agnes, nobody but you. You done lost the hair round the head and ain't no grease gonna bring it back, so I ain't talking 'bout no hair. You got a good case for the disability. Them same clinic doctors see you in the condition you in sure as hell gonna fix up the papers you need for the disability. What you mean you ain't begging? You hear me say something 'bout begging? The cold done settle in the toes, they all crooked, one on top of the other, and I hear tell you gots to sit when you does your lady ironing. How long you think you gonna be able to work like that? You gots to start looking out for self. Thirty-three years you been married up with Jasper, and thirty-three years Jasper momma name on the insurance policy. Eight children you give to Jasper. I seen you lay three of the finest children in the grave, and, Agnes, I cry for you and I cry with you. Then, Jasper up and die, find myself crying with you then. Damn if I ain't cried for you when I find out Jasper ain't left you nary a cent. You done good by them other five ones. Five pretty girls, and they married up to them service fellows and living all over. Don't come telling me the Lord gonna take care of you. You ain't no dim person, Agnes. You 'bout as bright as any of us on this here bus, and you is old enough to know the Lord wants us to help him help us. You sit right there waiting for the Lord, he sure ain't gonna send no doctor to you. While you still got the use of them there feet, you best truck on over to the clinic and get them disability papers I started telling you 'bout.

Okay. I'll see you later. Now, don't stump them feet getting off this here bus.

Hey, Essie Mae. Come and sit down by me. Girl, you looking good. Don't go flashing them long nails at me. Keep them fangs to yourself, and don't bring me no biscuits you done make to me. Your biscuit dough done a clean job under them there things. How you work with them long things?

Vernon treating you good these days? How things going for you at the store? When the last time "Miss Wear It One Time" been in to shop? I declare, Essie Mae, some people going fool trying to keep up with friends. The thing that gets me, they ain't no

48

friends. Girl, if I *had* the money, I never set foot in that fancy store where you work. Why? How I gonna know if I be buying the same dress "Miss Wear It One Time" ain't done buy and make the big impression and bring the dress back the next day or two?

Now, that one ain't got no personality, but she got the attitude. She act like her whole family dead. She don't bother with them up the road. How come I know? Her momma been at the usher union last month, and I just happen to ask how the daughter Marsha doing. Essie, Ms. Grayson never look me in the eye. She been too shame. Come telling me, well you know how it is; when the children husband travel lots, they gets to go, too. But Marsha, she doing alright.

Hey, Ruby, come sit by me. Ain't that been some mess at that funeral? All them years and all them children and that ain't the husband, but he be the children daddy. Here we is all waiting for the body in the church and the real wife done come and take the body. I blames me for not being outside the church when all that take place 'cause I listen to Blanche. Blanche tell me the church too small and can barely hold the family, and I best get in early to get a seat. Being feeble like I is, I ain't too good for standing long.

Now, you take Reverend South, he be so glad seeing all them folks in church, funeral or not he gets carried away. I declare, if preaching gonna get a body in heaven, Reverend South gonna sure put 'em in. But, Ruby, like I been saying, I sitting in church just looking around, and people I ain't seen in so long talking and catching up on happenings. No, honey, not me. I minds my business. When I in God's house, I does no talking; I listens. I notice the usher come up front whisper to Fannie at the organ, she rolls the eyes. Then, Fannie gets up and goes in the back. We is all looking round, and the church too quiet. Reverend South, he come to the front of the church, clear he throat, and say the funeral not gonna be held at the church 'cause the body been taken. I wants to know where 'cause I ain't gonna let Lucille bury Jake and I don't see Jake body in the grave. Everybody talking and asking questions wanting to know the name of the church so we can all get there for the funeral. Reverend South say he don't know nothing, and may the good Lord bless us for coming. Then, he done up and leave.

I gets out of the church fast as these ol' legs take me. Six family cars all line up, the hearse in front, flowers all over the street, the door to the hearse wide open, and the undertaker talking to Lucille children. I looking for Lucille. Mother Bennett, the church mother, in the first car fanning like mad 'cause Lucille done faint. What she got to fan 'bout? Lucille faint not she. I grab Lucille and put the smelling salt to the nose. Never you mind, Ruby, you see me at funerals I got my smelling salt in my pocket-book for sure. I gets Lucille to come round, and I had the devil getting sense in her head. I thinking, Lucille out she mind when she tell me Jake wife done take Jake. What kind of shit this be. Lucille Jake wife. Ain't they been married near to forty years and got fourteen children? Lucille tell me, when they get to the church, another hearse been parked right in front of the church, and the lady been standing there with the sheriff from another county, and he sure got the papers to take Jake.

Now, that be a dirty shame. I tell Lucille there ain't nothing she can do and no need to stay 'cause she better off being home. People sure as hell gonna talk now. That lady had everything planned. She wait good 'til Lucille sign funeral papers, then she come to town with her sheriff, undertaker, and them men folks to pick up Jake.

Sure, I knows what done take place. Lucille ain't got a pot to piss in. Them fourteen children all grown. I hear tell they mad as hell with Lucille 'cause Lucille been knowing 'bout that lady all them years and done nothing to make Jake get things straight. No, Reverend South don't know Jake ain't married to Lucille. You been knowing? Well, Ruby, if I ain't been knowing, how come you think somebody know? They done present themself in this town as husband and wife. You, just like me, done accept them. How the hell we gonna know different? I so mad right now at Jake. Why? 'Cause he done fool me, that be why.

Ruby, remember when Jervey die and we all at the funeral, and Minerva crying, and Reverend South just a ranting and raving, and the church all happy in the homegoing for Jervey? Minerva crying out loud, "Oh, my Jervey gone. Don't leave me, Jervey. Oh, Jervey, you done slip away. Why did you go, Jervey? Don't leave me, Jervey." A little, short lady pitched out of a seat in the back of the church, run up to the casket, bang she fist on the casket, shake she body, stamp she feet, throw she little head back, put she hands on she hips, and yell out loud, "My husband. Jervey my husband. Lord, look at my husband." Fannie done forget how to play the music. The choir done choke up, the spirit done left Reverend South, and Minerva climbing over the pew trying to get to that little lady.

The funeral been over. I ain't never seen undertakers get a casket out a church so fast. I still don't know to this day how they get that little lady out the church. No, she ain't pass through the back of the church 'cause I always sit near the back of the church 'cause I likes to see the family action. They done put her out through Reverend South office door. Ruby, that woman ain't been no fool. Jervey been she legal husband. Minerva ain't been back to church. No, now that ain't true, ain't nothing wrong with the heart. It be she head that be the trouble. I telling you what I know. Minerva ain't dealing with a full deck no more. They tell me every time Minerva see a short lady, she try to fight the lady. Honey, the mind done gone from Minerva.

Estell sick in the head. How she let them children of hers bring all that stuff home and they ain't got the first job is too much for me. She wrong to uphold them in wrong. No, she ain't never been one to check on she children, and anytime folks try to tell her 'bout them bad ass children of hers, she always gets to saying how folks jealous of her. The other day the police done come and take the two boys to jail. Then, the truck come and haul all the furniture that been new. No, the cars still in the yard. I guess they be the next to go, but I hear say them boys got the cars in the girl friend name. So that be a different story.

Girl I been too glad to hear 'bout Laura son, Danny. He win the full money to that doctor school. Oh, he done been for the four years. He well on the way now. He be just like the mail lady and the mailman. Rain or shine, that Danny sure gonna throw the newspapers. Laura is one sweet momma. Everybody on that street done lend a hand to raising Danny. I declare, that Danny belong to everybody. The church give Danny the suitcases when he come out first in the high school. Come time for the four year school, the church step in again and give Danny the coat. Now, we all know Danny need the coat for the cold place where he gone.

What I like 'bout it is Danny and he momma stay sweet and ain't even trying to put on airs, like some folks we know. What you mean when you look at me and say what I mean when I say "folks we know"? You know Juanita; I know Juanita. You know Dollie; I know Dollie. Well now, ain't they folks we know? Ain't Juanita and Dollie the same folks that splash water when we at the bus stop in the rain and pretend they don't see us while they passing by in the car? Ain't Juanita and Dollie the same folks we done collect the money to help send off to school when they momma and daddy low on the money? Ain't they done finish the school, working the good paying jobs, and still don't see nor know you neither me? Sure, they put on the airs, but I got news for them two. They up and die, the undertaker gonna do them up just like you and me. Only way that don't happen 'cause ain't no body for the undertaker to work on. Them two need to change.

Remember when Herbert die and the family had to beg the fellows to be pall bearers? That gonna be the same way with that Juanita and that Dollie. Honey, them people down on that end got long memories. Juanita had the tire blow out on the car right in front of Jake Grill. 'Bout seven fellows been standing round. If they lend a hand to help, I ain't riding this here bus this day with this fool ass driver acting like the devil behind him for sure. No, not a one. Tell me she sit in the car 'bout five minutes waiting for them fellows to lend a hand. She finally get out of the car, don't speak a word to them fellows, go into Jake place to call one of them trucks to pull the car. Must have been inside Jake place 'bout five minutes. Gone back outside, them spinning things on the tires all gone. You know what I mean. The hubcaps all gone. Fellows still standing all in the same spot, and ain't nobody saying nothing. Like I been trying to tell you, it pays to be nice to folks. It don't cost a thing to be nice. She best be glad it ain't happen nighttime.

I know one thing, Ruby. I got better sense not to put a house on land ain't got my name on a deed file somewhere. Who did that? That same Dollie, who try to be so smart. She marry that fellow been in service and then move the house she granddaddy give her on the husband momma land. The fool done add a room to the house and done brick the house. The husband done been separated from the service going 'bout three years, and ain't hit a lick of work yet. Oh, she say he looking for work, but he be in the special field, and he got to wait for the special field to open. No, she ain't driving all them miles to work. Listen to what I getting 'round to telling you.

The husband done put Dollie out, and she back living with she momma and daddy. Now, they say Dollie doing something they call the litigation, whatever that mean. Anyhow, whatever it is,

Dollie can't move the house 'cause she done put the granddaddy house on the same spot a house been before, and that dog she done marry up with saying the house been there for years. Proof? I been telling you all along the granddaddy give Dollie a old house. No matter where you put the house, the house still a old house. The only thing new 'bout that house is them bricks and the new room. Sure, the house been fix up inside, but it still be the old granddaddy house. Folks best remember where they done come from 'cause they just might have to go back. Dollie back, but she ain't change a bit.

Seems like this bus ride gets longer every day. Ain't able to put my finger right to it, but many is the time I just wants to ride this here bus and not get off when come time for me to get off. Then, I say, "Lord. Thank you, Jesus, for getting me started on another day."

Ruby, I was gonna tell you the other day I been to the hospital to visit John. You know how I is. I visit every room on the floor. I don't have to know folks to ask how they feeling. Anyway, I going down the hall from room to room saying hello and just minding my business, and, girl, I been too upset. Guess who been in the hospital? Well, you know nobody seen Zeke for a long time. I ain't had know that been Zeke. I hear my name call, I look round, I ain't see nobody I know. Then, I hear my name call again. I go over to the bed where I hear my name call from; all I see is them big frog eyes. That all been left of Zeke. Everybody know Zeke by them frog eyes. I say, "Zeke, what you doing in the hospital?" He tell me, "Minnie, take a good look, girl. I down for the last count this time." Sure enough, I take a good, hard, long look. Zeke been on the downside for sure.

I visit in the room, talking and trying to cheer Zeke up. I had to hold up the big head on that little neck to give Zeke a drink of water. I telling you this now 'cause Zeke come to town and nobody know where he from. He all the time sing the blues songs.

54

That be why they call Zeke *Blues Man*. Course now, the children all call Zeke *Frog Eye* when Zeke not 'round to hear. I spend time with Zeke but been down there to visit John. Zeke tell me, "Minnie, I ain't gonna sing my song no more." I say to him, "Zeke, man, you the *Blues Man*; you always gonna sing the blues."

Zeke grab my hand, Ruby, and he done put a hold on me. Zeke tell me he got to sing he song. I say, "Hush up, Zeke. I well know the song you sing when you been hit by the train. There you be all break up in this same hospital, and some fool done slip you some ol' rotgut shine. You drunk up and singing, 'You got me down now, but I won't worry. I'll be up again some day.' " Sure enough, I tell Zeke he be lucky. Keep the faith man, sing the same song, and don't give up. Ruby, how them eyes been popping and rolling, and he hand just a grabbing and holding my hand. Gal, that been like the death hold for sure.

Zeke say, "Minnie, these pains running through my body, and I just want to steal away." The sweat done start rolling off Zeke, and I too scared. I start wiping the sweat off Zeke, and I never in my life been so glad to see a nurse. The nurse ask me to leave 'cause it be time for Mr. Montgomery shots. I still standing, talking to Zeke and waiting for the nurse to give that Mr. Montgomery the needle. The nurse looking at me, I wiping Zeke and saying to myself, she sure ain't in no hurry to shoot the needle to Mr. Montgomery. That Mr. Montgomery gonna be dead, if he life 'pending on what in that needle.

I look at the nurse and say, "Sure is hot, ain't it?" She say, "If you say so." I said, "I done say so, ain't no need to say so again."

The nurse tell me, "Miss, you have to leave now; its time for Mr. Montgomery shots." I says to the nurse, "Ain't you gonna take care of that Mr. Montgomery? 'Cause I sure ain't stopping you, and anyhow I down here visiting with Zeke and ain't got nothing to do with that Mr. Montgomery and he shots."

Then, Ruby, the nurse say, "Look, Miss, if you don't leave I will get security." I getting hot then, Ruby. Zeke holding my hand and singing "Steal Away," and I ain't been to see John yet, and visiting hours gonna be over. I tell the nurse, "Call security 'cause I gonna tell security how you got somebody name Mr. Montgomery dying 'cause you ain't giving the needle."

The nurse leave the room, and she back in no time with two security folks. One ask me, "What's the trouble?" I say trouble it ain't, but death it gonna be if that Mr. Montgomery don't get he shots. Zeke start singing the song, "Do Lord, Lord, remember me. When I sick and can't get well, Lord, remember me. Oh, do Lord remember me, ol' Zeke Montgomery."

I say, "What that you say, Zeke?" Ruby, I be the fool. All the years Zeke been in town not a soul know Zeke last name be Montgomery. All I ever been know was Zeke the Blues Man. Lock me up? No, Ruby, I tell them security folks the gospel truth, that I ain't been know the nurse meant Zeke when she come in the room saying it be time for Mr. Montgomery shots. Anybody else tell me Zeke name be Montgomery, I sure take 'em down on that. I been to see Zeke two times after that. Why I stop going? Well, you been anytime? Well, alright then. Them two times I been, Zeke ain't even know I been. He just there singing the song "Steal Away." Zeke ain't never hurt a soul that I know 'bout, 'cause if he did, I be the first to know.

Life done come full circle for Zeke. He done sing the blues all the young days; now he down and singing the spiritual. How I know what going on with Zeke? How you know, Ruby? How anybody but Zeke and God know? I know one thing; Zeke had a chance to look back. That ain't gonna happen to everybody.

I declare, this road need to be closed. The driver ain't even trying to dodge the potholes. He mad as hell this morning. One thing for sure, when he hit the hole and his ass hit the seat, my ass got more fat, and I hanging in this seat for sure.

John? Oh shit, I forgot 'bout John. The tree fall on John. He still laid up. Both the legs been broke up. He home now. I hear tell he on the list for a home nurse. John ain't never gonna be the same no more. Them leg bones old, and John ain't no spring rooster. He be he own weatherman now. Them legs sure gonna tell when it ready to rain.

Sure, it been a accident, but money coming in every month sure don't stop them pain in the legs. Mind? No, he still fresh. Lula say she been cooking and cleaning for John fore he on the home nurse list. Lula say John come telling her only he legs break, and everything else together strong, and he be in the need of something. Lula say she well know what that old goat think, and she tell him she, too, in need of something. Lula say John start to grinning and say, "What dat you need? 'Cause John got it for you." Lula say John put the money for her on the dresser by the picture of Essie, the wife that done gone away with that railroad man a long time ago. Anyhow, Lula say she done finish the work, then she look down at John and say "What you got I ain't needing, but what I gonna do is get the hell away from you." Lula say she only done that work a few times to kind of help out with her social security. She baby sitting now, and she done tell me that a man sitting ain't for her.

Evelyn, see them new buildings over there? We got us a new lawyer. Now, that one we be proud 'bout. He belong to Bessie Mae. No, you wrong Evelyn. He ain't the one we call *Water Melon Man*. That one we call Water Melon Man be a slick one. He been trucking water melons up north 'bout seven years fore he get tangle up and get in jail. It been in all the papers how he done sell the water melons, then he done take the truck the water melons been take up there in and done change it into what they done call a *floating* card game. How he do that? I hear tell Water Melon Man take the whole top of the truck off and make

57

the top low, then he put water melons on the top of the truck. Then, he done fix up the inside of the truck nice, with a little bar, tables, and chairs. He done push the back end of the truck in and done make a new back end and had water melons on the end of the truck. While he driving round selling water melons— which he ain't been selling 'cause he had to leave enough on the top to cover the top—ain't nothing but card playing going on in that truck.

He been selling a few from the back part of the truck. Girl, he had to sell *some* water melons. Them people up north crazy 'bout water melons. He sell a few off the back end of the truck to make everything look alright. No, it ain't been a truck big as one of them eighteen wheel truck, but they tell me it been a big one.

Way I hear it, they had a shoot out in the truck. Something done gone down sour. How the police gonna know what going on in the truck? Them people up north don't talk like you folks down south. The police caught the devil when they get to the truck. Water melons all over the street. Children, momma, daddy, grand-daddy, grandmomma, and everybody all in the street grabbing them water melons. Some whole, some busted, and some all shoot up. They done find water melon and man all shoot up. Three dead body been in the truck. Water Melon Man in jail up north now, and ain't a thing he brother the lawyer can do. He done gone up north and get greedy, and it sure ain't done a bit of good.

Wife? That gal he married been gone. She ain't been from 'round here. Bessie Mae talk everything; she ain't like me. Everybody knows I mind my business. I bet she ain't talking 'bout Water Melon Man. What that boy name be? Let me think here a minute. Yeah, that be he name. He name be Alfred. They done start to call him Water Melon Man 'cause he done been catch in old man Pinckney water melon field stealing water melons. Old man Pinckney never did press charges 'cause he know Bessie Mae and she daddy. Water Melon Man pay the price then. He work all summer for old man Pinckney and never did get a penny.

But that lawyer brother is something else. That fellow got class. He don't try to hide the fact that he brother in jail. I bet that be the cause he got so many people going to him. He starting out just like the song; he gonna make it 'cause he trying.

Water Melon Man got a lot of time for the killing. No, he close to thirty-five now. He much older than the lawyer fellow. No, don't go asking me 'bout them girls. I ain't getting into that. I gots no money for a lawyer, and Bessie Mae got all the free lawyer time with the lawyer son. I keeps telling you, I ain't no fool. I knows when to keep my mouth shut.

You know, Ruby, so much done happen to the good folks we knows. Now, you take Brother Coates. All the land he done sweat for all them years he own in name only. On the papers it ain't no more his. That man and the wife, Lizzie, done all any good, Christian family could do in raising them children. They just gots to be strong folks to live through all they done been through. Sure, all seven of them children come up through the Sunday school, and they all been in the church. They biggest mistake been to *listen* to the word, and not to *live* by the word. Ruby, how in the hell whole family seven children be crooks? Them two girls done pick up them men folk, drunk them up in them motel and hotel rooms. Them brothers all done take turns beating and robbing them men folks. Then, the police done set the trap with the *unknown police*. You knows what I mean, Ruby, when nobody knows the law folks? What you say they is call? Undercover? Well, whatever they is call, they done trap all seven. They tell me them five boys been flashing big money all over the bottom court cross town. Talk been out they cut the deck of cards, and the two high card holders pull the job off each time them girls drunk up them men folks.

Ruby, who got money for one lawyer these days? Brother Coates done put up all he land to them lawyers for them no 'count children. Honey, they got them on every charge but murder. Sister Lizzie sing so the other Sunday, Sister Ethel had to take her down. Honey, the folks start to clapping and the tears start to falling, and not a eye been dry when Sister Lizzie keep on singing the song "Lord, I Have Tried". The good Lord knows they done try. Brother Coates tell me hisself that the land don't mean a thing to him 'cause he been gonna leave it to them children anyhow. So, since they done mess up land he done fix up, they land done gone to pay for them lawyers. Brother Coates and Sister Lizzie gets to live in the old house 'til they die.

They is hurting, Ruby. For sure, them old, good folks is hurting 'cause I see it. I say to Brother Coates, "You done work so hard all these years to get land, and now you and Sister Lizzie ain't got nothing left."

Ruby, Brother Coates look at me in the eye and say, "Sister Minnie, all that I done had belong to God. He done give and He done take it away, and I ain't gonna question the Lord why. So I keeps the faith and say, 'Blessed be the name of the Lord.' The Lord works in mysterious ways, and just maybe he done see fit to take all my children off these here mean streets to save them from maybe getting killed. I got to believe that, just maybe, this gonna be the changes that done take place to change all of them. My Bible tell me 'bout them changes and I gonna keep on praying for them changes to take over my children. Now, Sister Minnie," says Brother Coates, "I ask you to pray for them children 'cause I know prayer don't change *things*, prayers changes the *people* that causes things to happen." Ruby, after I done sit and talk some more with Brother Coates, he done lift my spirit.

Don't it seem like this here bus ride getting longer? We coming up to Veronica stop. Now, I like her. She is one nice white lady.

You know what she done tell me?—And, Ruby, I ain't had to ask her a thing. We just been riding this here bus and got to talking. Ruby, it ain't 'portant who done talk first. We done start to talk. That the 'portant thing. That be the big problem now, everybody waiting for the other to talk first.—Anyhow, Veronica tell me that she friends try everything to try to get she to move from where she been living over thirty years. All she friends done move from the city 'cause *we* done move all over this city. Veronica done tell me she and that black family next to her door getting along real good, and when something done happen to anyone in them houses, they all pitch in to help.

Now, guess what? All of them that done move out of this city done find that they done sell off them pretty old houses at a loss just to get away. Now, they done wake up to find what they thought they escape from right next door. Oh yeah, a lot of them moving back in this city, but they squeezing us out. What you mean, how they gonna do that? Ruby, I telling you now like I been telling them others, this ain't no time to sit home. You gots to get out to them community committee meetings to find out what going on. When it done get in the paper, it done gone far, and it gonna happen if we ain't keeping the eye and ears open.

Ruby, they buying up all them old houses, fixing them up, the tax rate done jump up, and all them old peoples living in them neighborhoods on social security, and them folks done cause the value of them house to jump up. Them old people ain't got no money to pay them higher taxes. Next thing you know, they gonna be long gone. You know what I mean, Ruby? They ain't gonna be living in they own house no more. Them same old people gone north years ago done save and buy them houses. Well, Ruby, I been north one time, and I ain't gonna go no more.

I guess you don't member my Cousin Geneva been married to Sonny Boy? Well, anyways, Sonny Boy done treat Cousin Geneva so bad, Cousin Geneva gone to New York and take the four babies. Sure they been babies. They been one, two, three, and four year old. Them years sound like they be babies to me. Cousin Geneva take up with a man up there, and that man treat them four babies like he done put 'em in Cousin Geneva. Cousin Geneva write and tell me how good the job been up there. I gone and stay a little over a year. Ruby, I ain't never seen people work, drink, and party so hard in all of my born days. Girl, here I be new in New York, and I trying to keep up doing them same thing. Got to the place where I ain't seen the inside of a church for weeks. Now, Ruby, you know that ain't like me. Girl, I let the good times roll, and I save my money, honey. Course now, that been what I gone up to New York to do, and that been to save money.

Things start to get a little slack twixt Cousin Geneva and me. I had the understanding I pay her so much a week for my room, then I take care for my food. Now, Ruby, you been knowing me for a long time, and you knows my word be my bond. When I done tell you something I gonna do, I gonna do just that. I take to notice every time Cousin Geneva and them friends of hers get together, they drinking and having the good time; then, I start to drinking and having a good time. Then, all of a sudden, Cousin Geneva start to talk 'bout how the family live off family people and don't carry the load. Now, I sure ain't no fool, and I done hear what I done hear. It ain't no lie when they say whiskey done loose the mouth. Ol' fool me, I still living with Cousin Geneva, and she ain't never to this day tell me she want me to pay more board money.

Cousin Geneva friend Martha had us over on Long Island for a party 'cause the family Martha been working with done gone down to Florida for vacation. Honey, we been having the time of our life. That been a pretty place. Neighbors? Honey, ain't been no neighbors for miles around. Them been some real rich folks. That house been all by itself with all them pretty trees and flowers. It had a bunch of them little, short trees too. What you say they is call? Shrubs? Well, they been fancy looking, with all kinds of shapes.

Now, I gonna tell you how sometimes your own people can do things to make you feel bad. I ain't never hide the fact that I never finish school. Well, Cousin Geneva did finish the eleventh grade. That as far as the school went where we been going. There I been in the kitchen, whipping up the upside down pineapple cake.—Everybody say I the best at making the cake that done taste one I done cook.—I hear all this laughing, and naturally, I want to get in on the laughing, too. I pick up my gin, take a sip, and start to join in on the fun. Then, strange things done come over me. I done swear I hear my own self talking in the other room. I take another drink and say to myself, girl, you ain't in that room; you right here in this kitchen. I listen up, and I hear my voice say, "Cousin Geneva, you so good to take me from down south 'cause you know I been hungry and had just one pair of shoes and hardly no clothes, and, Cousin Geneva, you been so good to me; you let me stay in your house, and you give me all the money I needs. Lord knows, I don't know what to do to show you how glad I is you is my Cousin. Cousin Geneva please let me cook you my favorite cake. I gonna cook upside down pineapple cake just for you."

Well, Ruby, it ain't been so much Cousin Geneva making fun of the way I talk 'cause I from over by the Island. She be from the same place; she just done been north all them years, and her talk done change some. It hurt 'cause she in that room lying on me. So help me God, Ruby, Cousin Geneva ain't never give me a dime. I work in that bean field for that money to get me to New York. After I get there, Cousin Geneva tell me it gonna be twenty-five dollars a week board. Every Friday, I pay Cousin Geneva first. Then, I put aside what I put to my mind I gonna save. Come hell or high water, what I save I ain't touching. Ruby, when I say I gonna save so much a week, that exactly what I gonna do. I never just put the money aside. I hide it good 'cause I had every other Thursday off. Then, that be the day I takes my money and my book to the bank. I makes sure they done put down on my book what is suppose to be on it.—I know something bad done happen years ago when I been little. Course now, that been done happen long fore I been to New York.—Anyhow, getting back to Cousin Geneva lying on me. Honey, let me tell you, I throws back my head, put that glass with that gin to my mouth, and drink every drop. I been in that room in no time flat. The laughing still going on, and Cousin Geneva having the time of she life.

Ruby, I always did have long hair, and everybody always did say I had a heavy head of hair. I ain't bragging now, but when it done been wash, straighten, and curl, honey, I been in my glory then. Even to this day, I keeps my hair fix. I keeps it up under this here net for work. I lets it down for church on Sundays, when I wears a black robe. I had to get Sister Mable straight when I first start on the choir 'cause I put the white handkerchief round my neck in back to keep my robe clean from my hair. Sister Mable keep on picking at me and nobody else. Mind now, Ruby, Sister Mable ain't got hardly no hair. Anytime you go by she house, Sister Mable got six pink sponge rollers in she hair, and that take care all of her hair. Stop laughing, Ruby, that the gospel truth. And you know what done happen at the church? Some of them other choir members doing a little tucking, themself, with a white handkerchief. Girl, it cost money to get them robes clean, and they ain't just white. Them robes is white on white, and you know how Reverend South always brag on his choir looking good. He gets to feel mighty proud when we travel with him and do the twelve tribes at all them churches in the country. Honey, them folks at them country churches know how to treat people. Reverend South always gets us there early, so we gets to eat. Ain't nothing gonna beat good singing on a full stomach.

Anyway, I walks up to Cousin Geneva, snatch off she wig. Cousin Geneva screaming and holding she bald head, and I mean bald head 'cause it ain't been but 'bout eight little, short plaits on she head. I bet nobody in that room laugh at me then. I done throw that wig on the floor and jump on it good. Good thing Cousin Geneva been my cousin 'cause, anybody else, I done throw on that floor and I been on top for sure. That man that take up with Cousin Geneva ain't been there 'cause he been a porter on the train, and his run done take him to Florida. Let me see now, his name been Macy, and he tell me he been from the Florida panhandle, wherever that is. Anyways, Ruby, like I been telling you, he been a good man. He see them four children through school, and they all got good college training, and doing big things. They comes down south for the family reunions, and they just as nice as nice is. He ain't doing too good in the health way now. I hear tell he done had a stroke and kind of sickly like.

I left Cousin Geneva, gone back to New York, and pack my things all I could get in my suitcases. What I had left out, I done lay five dollars on Cousin Geneva bed with a note tell she that be for a spread I take. Ruby, I put the rest of my stuff in that spread, clean up the room, and left just like that. Where I go? I been right up the avenue to Rebecca Ringly rooming house. You see, Ruby, I been working for some good people, and it ain't like me to just up and leave a job. I stay on that job near 'bout six months, and Rebecca Ringly been round New York for a long time. Everybody know she run a straight house. I pay she the same twenty-five dollars I been paying Cousin Geneva, but Rebecca Ringly give me a receipt every time.

Now, you see, if I had know that Cousin Geneva let that whiskey cause she to lose she common sense and just tell me she want more board money from me, I be 'blige to pay more 'cause I living in she house and family be family. That been a good lesson for me, Ruby. To this day, I gets a receipt for everything, and I got a drawer at home where I keep 'em all. Many been the time when I say, if I had get receipts from Cousin Geneva, she by no means could get away with telling that big lie on me. I never look toward Cousin Geneva house no more 'cause I catch the subway down from she house, so I ain't had no reason to walk up the avenue.

Life sure is strange, Ruby. All of a sudden everybody having family reunions. Honey, this be the good part. We done had 'bout twelve of them reunions. Hot dog, Cousin Geneva, done show up at this one. Like I done tell you, I don't like leaving home, and I ain't never been to a reunion no place but here. Every time the reunion down here, everybody want me to cook my upside down pineapple cake. I good at them cakes, and I ain't shame to say it. This time I throw in a big pot of okra rice. I good at that, too. Mine ain't slimy like most folks' is. I good at the heron and rice, too. Girl, don't start me to talking 'bout food, 'cause I slings a good spoon when it done come to them rice dish. This time, I done add the sausage to the okra and rice. Soft? No, Ruby, mine been just as grainy and loose, but, girl, it be fluffy.

I done spot Cousin Geneva right away 'cause, out of all of them people, she walking round in high heel shoes and stocking on she feet, with a two-story wig on she head. Everybody else got on them t-strap dress, shorts, pants, or just a dress a body don't mind messing up with watermelon or barbecue sauce dripping.

I guess the devil done rear up horns in me 'cause I bide my time real good. When it done come time to eat all of them sweets, I walks over to Cousin Geneva, looks she straight in the eyes again, like I done on Long Island all of them years ago. No, Ruby girl, it been near 'bout to thirty-five years since I done seen Cousin Geneva last. Ain't I just done get through telling you all them

66

four children done finish with they college training? I says to she, "Cousin Geneva, I been waiting a long time to give you this here upside down pineapple cake 'cause I always member how you say I beg to give you one when I been staying with you in New York."

Ruby, you should a been there. Gal, I declare, Cousin Geneva wig look like it done rise one more story high. She eyes done get big, tongue done get heavy, she heavy breathing, and can't say a word. Ruby, I know she been just waiting for me to throw that cake in she face. That nice man Macy sitting right by she side. Nobody but Cousin Geneva and me know what going on twixt she and me. I been looking good, girl. I just had my hair wash, straighten, and curl, and it been curl that new way up in the front and just hanging loose with curls under in the back. When the wind blow, my hair flying round my face and back. I feel good 'bout that 'cause I know it ain't flying off. I run my fingers through my hair in the back part of my head, put that cake right down in front of Cousin Geneva, and say, "For you, Cousin Geneva." Then, I talk to Macy and walk away, and I ain't look back. Honey, we had us a good time that day.

Don't ask me, Ruby, if she eat the cake. So much family to see and visit with, and everybody telling me they always like coming south for the reunion 'cause we fix more food, and we ain't shut up in them hotels and motel rooms eating food the family ain't done cook. I telling them how glad I is they enjoy the food, but wishing like hell I could sit in one of them hotel or motel room to enjoy what they done fix 'cause, Ruby, you know well as I do, them reunion work the hell out of a body. It be a good thing the family done decide to have it every two years. Well, yeah, I know you get to go every year 'cause, the year your side ain't got it, you got to go for you husband Ben side.

Girl, let me make you laugh. Ethel tell me she been to Boston for she family reunion, and they drive up to that motel they done sign all the family from down south in. Ethel say they had all the drinks a body can ask for. Now, Ruby, I ain't one to talk 'cause I minds my own business, but this be so funny, just got to tell you. Everybody know Ethel gonna drink long as she see it. Now don't get me wrong, I ain't faulting a soul for drinking 'cause, Lord knows, I done my part. Besides, Ethel be a hard working soul just like I is.

Ruby, let me tell you something. I drink so hard one weekend, I miss church and I miss work. I tell myself, fool, when you let that devil cause you to miss church and work, it be time to stop. I lose my job, how I gonna get money to get my hair fix? How I gonna get my robe clean? How I gonna pay my church support? How I gonna pay pastor support? How I gonna buy food? How I gonna pay light and water bill? I asking me all them questions. My head killing me with that bad hangover, and I say, fool, how in hell you gonna just live? And you know, Ruby, if them people at that phone company cut off my phone, well, I really be done. I bet I collar my ass real good and put this body in shape. Now, I ain't gonna lie and say I done stop altogether. I sips me a little gin from time to time, but it call what some folks call *nipping* at times. I ain't no different from them Catholic folks with they wine. I likes wine, too, but gin is the thing for me. You know, just a little in the morning when it be cold like this is now, and a fool bus driver late and got everybody standing in this cold. Don't you worry, Ruby. Just as sure as the good Lord let me finish this days work and I gets back home in my house, I gonna call his momma and tell she good how he drive and act like the fool. Ain't no reason for he to drive this bus like he be the bat out from hell fire.

Anyways, Ethel say she drinking and having real fun, and all them young ones dancing all over the place. Come time to eat, they all gone in another room. Ethel say so many people been there she notice that after they done keep putting more food in them serving dishpan things over them candle up under them pans. The nearer she get to the pan with she plate in she hand, ain't nobody coming from the kitchen to put more food in them pans. Ethel say she good and tipsy and hungry 'cause Old Crow wing flapping all over she stomach. Ethel love some Old Crow now, but Ethel drink what ever 'round in a bottle. Ethel say she 'bout ten people from the food pan when the food gone, and she look behind she and 'bout thirty people holding plates in they hand for food.

Mind now, Ethel brother Howard always did think he be smarter than them others in Ethel family. He the big dog. He been up in Boston close to fifty years. He been in Boston from a young fellow. He been doing construction work and start out with some Irish man, and they say that man depend on Howard for everything. Howard been the gang lead man and been the one to keep them men on the construction place 'til all that work done finish. That man ain't had no kin folk and done died and put all of them trucks in Howard name. They say them other people ain't been going for Howard to get all them trucks, but Ruby they ain't had a leg to stand on, 'cause that man had a will done made out, they say, 'bout four years fore he die that Howard be the one to get them trucks. Howard had a time after that. He had the trucks, but no place gonna use Howard trucks to haul to the construction places. but Howard outsmart 'em good. He been real friendly with them council people. Tell me he done a little work for this one and that one, and next thing you know, them trucks of Howard been moving and hauling just like before that man die. Howard smart, Ruby. He had all them driving for he to join in a union. Howard wife, Alice Jean, all the time sending pictures of Howard and the big shots down here from that newspaper.

One of the lady from that motel kitchen gone up to Howard and say something. Ethel say Howard get up and gone to the line and tell everybody not to worry, food be for everybody. Say Howard gone into the kitchen and been in too long for Ethel. Ethel say she know everybody done pay what they suppose to pay for each family 'cause Howard watch every penny like a hawk watch a bird. And, if you ain't paid, you ain't eating, not with Howard in charge.

Ruby, Ethel tell me she gone into the kitchen, and that food stack up in trays. That same lady that talk to Howard before telling Howard that too many people done take too much food, and that the food Howard looking at been being prepared for another family reunion starting the next day. Ethel say that, when she look at all that pretty brown fried chicken and them hunks of beef, fore she know what done happen she done gone by Howard, push that lady to the floor, and put she hands in the stack of beef, pushing the beef in she mouth. She done snatch up the pan of chicken, running through the door and yelling at everybody come and get it. Ethel say, at first the people ain't been knowing what been going on. She know she been hungry, and she gonna eat.

The lady call the police, and Ethel been 'rest for battery and stealing. Say Howard been too 'shame. He tried like the devil to talk them police out of 'resting Ethel, but Ethel been too tipsy to shut up and keep on yelling at the police. Say Howard try to tell the officer in charge who he is, but that ain't been the same officer of that district that know Howard. Howard sure ain't get no favor that day 'cause of who he is.

They had to drop the stealing charge from Ethel 'cause they done find that lady been working ain't been the one to be in charge of the kitchen that day. She been a stand in 'cause the lady who been schedule to work the kitchen call in with the flu, and somehow the count been wrong, and that done make the chicken and beef short. They give Howard the money back. Tell me the judge fine Ethel for pushing the lady down and charge Ethel with disorder toward the policeman. Ethel been jail in a place call Commonwealth up in Boston overnight, and Ethel tell me she done tell that policeman that she poor. They can't put she in the Commonwealth jail 'cause that be for the wealthy people. They done had to lock up Ethel 'cause Ethel so drunk from Old Crow and all that other stuff she been drinking. The law done say they done it to protect Ethel from she self. Tell me Howard been so out and done, he busy working to keep all the reunions down south now. Ethel swear she be in my family 'cause every time we got a reunion she gets to go where it be. She be full of fun, never a dull time when Ethel round.

Well, Ruby, you have a good day, and tell Ben I done ask 'bout him. Glad to know the children doing good. See you on the morrow, God willing.

Well, hey there, Connie. Lord, if you ain't the proud one this morning. Hi, Veronica. You sit right next to me here. I done hear that good news, Connie. I just waiting for you to get on this bus to tell me 'bout the blessing. Morris home from the hospital, and he talking 'bout going back to work. He be just like old Morris again. Good thing be been in good shape fore that accident. How long Morris been working on the waterfront? Forty-two years! Lord, that a long time for sure. By all counts Morris be dead 'cause that crane done drop almost square on Morris.

Now, Connie, you say Morris done tell you he standing by them crates, and all of a sudden, a white bird done fly in Morris face and push him back. Morris say he done put a fight getting that bird from he face, but that bird ain't giving up. Morris say he hear all them fellows yelling and running past where he been fighting that white bird that been pushing at him. Next thing Morris know, that crane done drop on he, and ain't nothing out but he head. Morris say he eyes open and looking straight up and ain't feel no pain. He just lying on that deck, saying over and over, "Lord, have mercy."

71

All them fellows run back to Morris, trying to lift that crane. They ain't budge that crane one bit. Morris ain't saying nothing to them fellows. Morris, he just looking straight up, saying, "Lord, have mercy."

They done call for them emergency people, and the fire department done get in on it, too. They all been 'round. They done get another crane and lift that crane off Morris.

I ain't been down on that waterfront and you ain't been down neither, Connie, but all them people say, when they hitch up that crane to pull that other one off Morris, a big ol' white bird been press flat on Morris, with them wings spread all over Morris, 'cept Morris face, which ain't been hit by that crane. They say that bird wings start to flapping slow, then fast, and all of a sudden, that bird fly up off Morris, straight up. And that white bird done get smaller and smaller and done gone, and ain't nobody alive been down on that waterfront know what done happen to that white bird. They is all alive, but they don't know 'til this day how to say what done happen with that white bird.

Them doctors say they ain't seen nothing like that. Ain't no bones break on Morris; ain't nothing wrong inside Morris. He just stay in that hospital bed saying, "Lord, have mercy." Morris ain't been moving a thing but he eyes and he hands. Now, Morris home and talking again. Praise the Lord! Them doctors say Morris scared to walk, and it gonna take time. That just go to show you what them doctors ain't knowing.

Veronica, I been right in church when Connie start to bring Morris back to church. All Morris done is sit in that wheelchair, Sunday after Sunday, saying, "Lord, have mercy."

I ain't ever in all my bone days gonna forget how last month Reverend South preaching 'bout Jesus making the blind man see and the lame man walk. When Reverend South done say, "rise and walk," ain't nobody know Reverend South been pointing at

Morris, 'cause when Reverend South gets carried away, that man pointing, jumping, and moving all over that pulpit.

Veronica, I know you ain't never been to service in our church, but that don't mean you ain't one day. You ain't able to hold to you seat when a miracle done take place. Connie knows I telling the truth. When Reverend South shout out "arise and walk" three times, honey, Morris pitch straight up in that wheelchair, running to the pulpit shouting, "Lord, have mercy."

Connie, you ain't been no slacker 'cause you crying, "Jesus, Jesus," and ain't no telling what I been saying 'cause I done jump out the choir loft behind the pulpit, in the pulpit grabbing Morris and Reverend South, and that whole church shouting praises to God. Honey, that been one time to rejoice.

So what Morris up to now, Connie? Is that true? Well now, if Morris wanting to get back to the water front but ain't up to working on Sundays no more, overtime or not, that be up to Morris 'cause he thinking God done send a message to heed. Morris up in age now for all that heavy lifting. Aint' he what they call the *lead man*? You gots to be careful with them men folk when it come to them jobs 'cause, see, it don't take too much for them to think they be useless when they ain't got no job to go to. Just be careful, girl, and let that man make up he own mind. Later on he can't throw nothing back at you when things ain't going right. Now, don't be no fool and tell Morris I done say that to you 'cause I wants Morris to always know that I minds my business.

Connie, out of all of us riding this bus, I can say that you and Morris got money, and it ain't touch you neither Morris head the wrong way. Morris always helping out people, and he always up on he church money. But you know, girls, money ain't everything. Just maybe the good Lord want Morris in church more often. Connie, you good, too. I know 'bout how you give all them vegetable to that shelter for them homeless people. Some folks just throw it away but, no, not you, 'cause it ain't rotten when it come from that vegetable place you got. How come some folks rather see food rot fore they gives it away, I ain't never gonna understand.

That song say, "I don't know what the future will hold." That be the truth 'cause, if we done know that, we just take our body to the undertaker right now, and that take care of that. Connie, don't ever change, honey; you too strong in what God want all he children to be.

I been meaning to tell you 'bout that new girl you got hired. Oh no, she nice and friendly, but she on that phone too much. I wants to pay for my vegetables and get on home, but every time I in the place, that girl on the phone talking. I miss my bus while she talking, I ain't gonna catch another bus going my way for a whole hour, and I ain't the only one she done pull that on. I telling you 'cause we be friends and in the same church, too. Them other folks gonna just stop coming, and you ain't gonna know why they ain't buying from you no more. What? Oh, that be easy. You got one of them call waiting line? No. Okay, all you got to do is start calling that place of yours twixt four thirty and five thirty. That be the time she hot on the phone 'cause you done gone for the day. I bet you ain't gonna get through to you own place. I feel sure, Connie, you gonna take it from there.

Well, Veronica, I been telling my friend Ruby how nice you is. Ruby don't come this far to get to work. She not working on the Island now. How things on your job? Sure took them folks quite a spell to take your word on putting in all that makeup for us folks. All them years we been just putting on the face whatever they been telling us. Now you in charge behind the counter at the store, and you done put our colors up for sale, and you is now what they call the supervisor. You done gone one step further, too. You done hire two pretty, black girls to show how them colors look.

74

Oh! I been hearing 'bout you down at that store, Veronica. Course now, when they is talking, they ain't knowing I knows you. You done make two houses good and happy by giving them two girls them jobs. They daddy and momma so proud. They is telling everybody that gonna hear 'bout how they behind the counter store at the mall selling makeup. You done the right thing, 'cause I ain't never could understand how I gonna buy makeup when you done slap it on your white arm, smear it all around, and then tell me that it be just the color for me. I been in your store the other day, and I ain't seen you, but I seen all the people all 'round that counter just waiting in line for them girls to show how pretty them colors look.

You say the money pouring in 'cause sales going up? That be good for you, Veronica, 'cause you had sense to get in what they call *ethnic makeup*.

I meant to tell you fore I forget. I thank you for them samples you done give me. I ain't too much on the heavy stuff these days, but I spruce up real good for Sunday. I done give some to Lois, my granddaughter. Lord, don't let me get started on that child. She done swear she gonna be everything I ain't even heard 'bout yet. No, honey, she ain't but fifteen going on twenty-five when it comes to makeup and them clothes. She be a whip in school now. No. Her momma don't take to no dating at that age. Lois got friends she pals round with, and that way she ain't hanging on to no one fellow. Anyways, that's what it looks like to me.

Sure, I done tell her that you done tell me that, when she finish school, you gonna place her on a job 'cause that gonna help her with all that college money she gonna need. I sure does thank you, Veronica, 'cause the college jumping up every year asking for more money. It look like it gonna be rough, but by the Grace of God and friends like you, Lois gonna make it. I mention this to you 'cause I know you ain't got nobody to tell it to, but Lois been on the honor roll and is one of them national honor society girls. Her English teacher done tell her momma that, if Lois keeps her grades up, she gonna be in line for getting one of the scholarships. Now, ain't that a blessing? No, Veronica, the teacher ain't said nothing 'bout it being full or partial; she just talk 'bout a scholarship and Lois keeping them grades up. I guess, the higher grades Lois gets, they gonna tell us more.

Proud! Sure, I proud, Veronica, but I ain't telling nobody on this bus 'cause they too quick to say I think my Lois so much. Well, I does, but I ain't wanting them to tell me they is glad for Lois 'cause they ain't gonna say it with gladness. They ain't gonna be happy for that child. Too many selfish people riding this bus. I knows them too well. They ain't fooling me. They just waiting like the fox in the hen house, just waiting for Lois to be caught off guard. I talks to Lois, always telling that child to behave, 'cause some folks take joy from the downfall of other folks.

But getting back to you, Veronica. How your boy Glen doing? Where he stationed now? Japan. That sure is a long way from here. What is the girlfriend name again? That alright, dear, I can't say that name. How you gonna spell that name? Lord, that a long spelling name. What you gonna call her name for short? Honey? Now, that sound sweet.

Veronica, you done the right thing to write that girl 'cause, just as sure as you done tell that Glen boy of yours that you ain't wanting him to bring that girl home to you for a daughter-in-law, you been gonna lose your boy. I hates to remind you, but you done lose one son by death, and here you is with a chance to get a daughter. I bet that girl gonna make you proud for sure. Oh, be damn what folks gonna say, Veronica. As long as Glen gonna be happy, ain't that what happiness all 'bout? I know you gonna be happy when that baby gets born. I just glad to hear he gonna send for you to be with them fore the baby come.

76

I sure gonna miss you. How long you say you gonna be gone? I guess I can do without talking to you that long. Ha ha ha ha. Course now a month gonna be a long time 'round a new baby and the newly weds. And I do mean *newly* weds. You done the right thing. No need to talk 'bout this 'round your job. All they need to know is that you gonna visit your boy. Don't even take the baby picture on the job; keep all of them out of your business. If they come to your house and the pictures up in the house, then you explain 'bout the baby. Then again, if it be me, Veronica, I ain't explaining nothing to nobody 'cause it ain't gonna be they damn business.

I pray that the momma and the baby gonna be safe. Them people so little. Sure hope the momma and the baby gonna be healthy. Don't you start worrying now, Veronica. I say a prayer for both of them, and God gonna hear. Right now, we gotta get you off. When you say you gonna leave? Next Saturday? I know you been packing and unpacking. Well, that be good. The weather over there just like it is over here.

What's that you say? No, I don't know 'bout her. She just start riding the bus last week. She get on here scared looking and still scared looking. Tell you what, why don't you sit by her tomorrow morning and see what you gonna get from her conversation like. Be sure to tell her ain't nobody gonna hurt her, and she can always sit by me over here. I ain't going over by her 'cause this right here is my seat, and everybody riding this bus knows this here my seat. Oh, I don't mind talking first, Veronica. You know I done talk to you first, but that child look so scared over there, I just as sooner stay over here like I gonna do anyway.

Yeah, they done send them to me, and I done cut them up. I ain't wanting nobody credit cards. I got the feeling you done put them folks up to sending me them cards. No, honey, not to me. I done seen what them credit cards done to some folks I know. I thanks you just the same, but I too much into laying away. Besides, when I wear my things, they done pay for. Some folks still paying on things, and they don't know where half them things is.

You must mean that navy blue suit. I glad you like it. I been real scared when I hear last week they done hit the mall store where you work. Veronica, them folks plain down fool now. How you gonna fight with one of them silver guns in the face? Don't be no fool, Veronica; that money ain't yours give them crazy fools what they want. They print money every day, but they sure ain't gonna make another you.

That be different. Rachel been walking from the grocery store when that boy been robbing them people, and she done walk slap in the middle. Rachel say it hit her good sense in the head when she see that gun in that boy hand. She drop them brown bags, start to running, and tell her feet, "Feet, help the body." Sure, she been scared. How come you think she done run like a bat out of hell? Rachel know that boy with that gun. That been Big Margaret boy, Dan. He be the same one that beat up Mr. Levi that got the pawn shop. Rachel been so scared she stay up in the country near on to a month. She ain't looking to this side 'til she get the word Dan been catch. Oh, he got to serve the time, Veronica. See, he been out on parole from beating up Mr. Levi. Now, he got to serve out them years plus what he done get for robbing that business store. They tell me Big Margaret done faint in the courthouse when they sentence Dan.

No, he ain't no only child. Big Margaret done had Dan on the change of life. It be 'bout eighteen years twixt Dan and Big Margaret other boy. That other boy real quiet like. Don't hear nothing 'bout him. No, he don't live down here. He been in the service and done retire with a family in Jersey. He been trying to get Big Margaret up to Jersey, but she all the time talking 'bout she got to do this or do that for Dan. She ain't got no excuse now,

78

'cause Dan in the pen. But she just like all them momma with them no good children, bust they butts to get to the pen every visit day they is allowed.

Veronica I just got to ask you this, and sure hope you ain't gonna mind, 'cause I is gonna ask you anyways. I know it close to freezing this morning, and this bus been real late, and we all standing in the cold waiting. How come you ain't got no stockings on them feet? You say you ain't cold 'cause you got a coat and gloves on? Them toes red, and you mean to tell me you got that heavy coat on but no stockings, and you ain't cold? That don't make no sense to me. I is telling you now like my momma done tell all us girls; when we is young and ain't taking care of the body, we gonna pay for in our old age. I keep that and done pass it on to my children. I sure hope I don't fall down 'cause I got on so much I be rolling like a ball. No joke now, Veronica; you best start putting on socks or stockings on them feet. See how I got socks and stockings on, and my feet done start getting heavy waiting for this bus this morning.

Okay, this your stop. Don't work too hard. I gonna look for you on the morrow, God willing, and the devil better not try to stop me, even if he be driving a bus.

Hey there, Julius. How you doing there, man? See old Pin Stripe lately? Man, Julius you sure ain't no good. I laugh every time I think 'bout Pin Stripe. Sure, I been at the wake. Pin Stripe been sharp in that suit he had on, too. Ha ha ha ha. I don't think I ever done see Pin Stripe when he ain't been in the bottle. Here I is at the wake for Pin Stripe brother Jessie, and I looks up and see Pin Stripe going to the casket. Next thing is I hear old Pin Stripe talking 'bout how good Jessie look. Then Pin Stripe sit down right in front of where I been sitting. Next thing I know, Pin Stripe done get up and gone and look down on Jessie again. Julius, Pin Stripe start crying, and it done get so bad with Pin Stripe, all them fellows he hang out with done hurry up front and help bring Pin Stripe to the seat.

I hear Pin Stripe tell Buck that Jessie look damn good in that pinstripe suit, and Jessie laid out in a suit just like his pinstripe suit. Buck telling Pin Stripe, "Sure, man, Jessie looking real good, and you gonna look good, too, 'cause everybody know you good for wearing them pinstripe suits. That's how you got your name, man."

Ol' Pin Stripe so drunk all he can say is, "Yeah, man, you right; I gonna be sharp just like Jessie."

Julius, all of a sudden Pin Stripe jump up and tell all them fellows he got to go, man. Pin Stripe let out a yell and done run out the church. We all sitting round talking, 'cause the undertaker don't leave them bodies in the church overnight hardly no more. See, now that be another thing. Jessie ain't been one to walk in the church when he been well, and Reverend South ain't been too much on laying Jessie out in the church. But because Sister Alma been in the church all them years, he been kind and let him lay out in the church. I still say, if he ain't been walking in the church by his own feet, how come six menfolk got to carry him out now. They ain't been playing no music, ain't been no singing.

All of a sudden, we hear this loud talking outside the church: "Turn me loose man; you better turn me loose. Let go, man. Damn it, I done tell you let go."

Then, we hear another voice say, "Man, don't do that. It ain't gonna do you no good. He dead, man; that be your brother in there, and you drunk, man. Come on, Pin Stripe. Man, you a cool dude; you ain't gonna miss that one."

Then, I hear somebody say, "Let go, man. Let go."

Somebody else say, "Don't do that, man; don't do that. Don't go back in that church."

I hear something like grunting and scraping, and it sure done sound like some fighting going on out in front of the church. I hear somebody say, "Let the M.F. go." I disbelieve my ears hearing that so loud in front of the church outside. All of a sudden, I hear this running in the church. I looks up to see good who that be running in the church at a time when a wake going on. It be Pin Stripe, running up to his brother Jessie in the casket.

I hear Pin Stripe say, "You dirty M.F., no wonder your dead ass look so good. I want my M.F. suit off your dead ass." Old Pin Stripe grabbing at Jessie and saying, "Give me my damn suit. They ain't gonna put my damn suit in the ground on your dead ass. Anybody buried in that damn suit, gonna be my black ass." Pin Stripe ain't been too drunk not to know his clothes when he see that suit.

Julius, you been right in church that night, and you know they done catch hell getting Pin Stripe to turn dead Jessie loose in that casket. Sister Alma been begging Pin Stripe to stop. Old Pin Stripe look at his old momma and say, "Momma, you wrong. Momma, you know you wrong; you know that my suit on Jessie."

Poor Sister Alma say to Pin Stripe, "That just one suit, son. You gots lots more."

Pin Stripe say to Sister Alma, "Momma, this is Friday and you done lay Jessie out in my Saturday suit, and I want my damn suit."

Good thing the undertaker come in then 'cause they tell Pin Stripe something. They push Jessie back down in the casket decent like, close it, and got the hell out of that church with Jessie.

Sure, I been at the funeral. I ain't seen you, neither, but that church been packed and, Lord, it ain't been no place for cars to park within miles. I don't know 'bout that, but, Julius, I know for sure I done get a good look at Jessie in that casket dressed to a T in that pinstripe suit, and he had on a black suit in that casket at his own funeral, and it ain't been no pinstripe in that black suit on Jessie in that casket.

Ol' Pin Stripe been right in church sitting with the family, and he sure as hell had on that pinstripe suit dead Jessie had on in that casket at the wake. That be the same suit Pin Stripe had on 'cause the whole neighborhood know Pin Stripe got seven pinstripe suits, and he wear one for each day. That be why he got the nick name Pin Stripe.

By the way, when you see Elmore last? No, he ain't working. I been telling him all along it ain't what you thinking, it be what you done say. No, that ain't the way it happen. Elmore tell me straight like you and me sitting here talking now on this bus. It ain't been nothing like you done say you hear. Elmore say all them been in the shop working, and he up under the car hood telling Harriet boy Mump that his boss done tell him who to vote for 'cause, if they vote for that other man running, they ain't gonna have no job 'cause the president they got now gonna keep things moving the way they is.—Now, you know and I know things moving, but they ain't moving for us like they should.—Anyhow, Elmore tell his boss he gonna do just what the boss tell him to do 'cause he sure does need a job, with his six children all in school. All the time Elmore saying that he know once he get in that voting booth he ain't gonna do like the boss tell him, 'cause only God and Elmore gonna know what he do. Instead of the fool keeping the mouth shut, he under the hood telling Mump how he done vote, not knowing the boss man done come up and hear everything he saying to Mump.

All them twenty-seven years Elmore been working in that garage fixing them cars and trucks. He a good mechanic.

His mouth still flapping, and he going on about how he been voting like he want to 'cause them others been kept in the dark, scared they gonna lose the job if they don't say they gonna vote the way the boss done say vote. Well, *he* gonna do like he always *been* doing. Listen to the boss, agree with the boss, and vote his own mind.

Prove what? How you gonna prove that business done fall flat off, and the boss done say a mechanic got to go? Elmore say the boss know he can't read too good, but he can figure out how to take them cars and trucks apart and put them back together. Anyhow, the boss call Elmore aside and tell Elmore he done enroll Elmore in the county technical school in some kind of auto mechanics class, and the class gonna last for nine weeks. Elmore been in that school three days and ain't been back. Sure, them children try to help the daddy. Elmore sitting in the class without the children.

Now, get this. Elmore gone down to the garage and tell the boss he don't need the class to fix cars and trucks, and he can fix them just like he been doing. The boss tell Elmore he sorry, but all them fellows got to go through the class. All them other workers half Elmore age and got much more schooling then Elmore. Gladys' boy J.T. working at the garage, and Gladys tell me J.T. say the boss man ain't said nothing to nobody about going to no school. Elmore ain't got a foot to stand on. Them fellows need jobs. They got children in school, and they ain't about to lose jobs the way things is now.

Catherine tell me he been through one day selling vegetables with his brother-in-law, Ralph. Man, where you been? Ralph been back in town. Seven years Ralph been in the pen and keep telling people he innocent. Poor Miss Vincent dead in the grave not knowing her boy finally free. She been dead about three years now. She been in a nursing home 'cause she put up everything she had for that lawyer for Ralph. No, now that ain't so. She tell Reverend South she ain't gonna let no public lawyer talk for Ralph.

Ralph had one child, a pretty little girl by that woman. Sure, she been white, but they been married. That been going on. Ain't nothing wrong with that. What wrong is when people don't mind they own business. Anyhow, that woman family turn the back on that child, and old Miss Vincent take that child and done good by her. That girl grow up just loving everybody. Sure, she know about her other people. Miss Vincent ain't hold nothing back from that child. It be a good thing she tell all 'cause you know how folks is in this town, can't mind they own business at all. Some folks mouth flapping all the time. Miss Vincent figure she best tell that child about everything firsthand. She been in and out of my house, and you know me, I minds my own business. Ain't for me to tell nobody a thing.

Anyways, like I been saying, when the word hit town that some man in the pen hospital in one of them states confess while he been dying about the killing he done back here, that child been in law school. She start the ball to roll in the right direction, and next thing I know, Ralph back in town, done buy Miss Vincent house back, and got it all fix up real good.

No, he ain't living in the house. He got the house out on rent. He staying over on the island on land he buy from old man Pearson. Say he don't like living in town no more. He been lock up so long in the pen and working on the pen farm, he use to being in open space now. I hear tell he got a good truck farm going. A lot of money. All I can say is he got a lot of money for them seven years in the pen.

Elmore smart with them hands, but dumb when it done come down to the common sense. Sure jobs gonna open up some now, but you got to have school smarts for all them technical things they is doing now. All the time this here bus been bumping and stopping over these here railroad tracks and potholds, I been try-ing to think of Ralph girl. It's a pretty name, but it reminds of that scary thing they call Dracula. Got it! That girl is name Drucilla. She love herself some Ralph, mind you. She take him with her to Atlanta for awhile.—Look like everybody going to Atlanta now. One time all you could hear was New York.—Anyways, I hear that she say her daddy need to get to know her 'cause, all that time Miss Vincent putting her through school, she ain't seen her daddy Ralph no more than 'bout seven or eight times. Sure, children can do good. 'Cause no daddy in the house, ain't no cause to be lowlife. Some got the daddy home, and they ain't worth a shit.

Excuse me for asking, Julius, what come of your boy Oscar? Last time I hear you been telling everybody he big in the Army. Oh! So you saying they jealous 'cause he getting too many stripes, and they start taking the stripes from him? Now, I do declare, that sure is something. Where he stationed now? Texas. When last you and Grace hear from him? Been that long, eh? You two plan on going to Texas? Ain't you got grands out there you ain't seen yet? Oh, so Oscar say they might be stationed someplace else, and for you and Grace to wait 'til they get where they going. How long you say they been stationed in Texas? Fifteen years. The same base? How about that, and for the past ten years he been waiting to go someplace else, and you and Grace been waiting to hear the word to come on. Well now, you know how the government can be. Them wheels turn slow sometime, just like old people.

Nice talking to you, Julius. Be sure to tell Grace you done see me and I ask 'bout your boy Oscar.

Good morning, Nurse Preston. How you be this morning? I know what you mean. Good to have a day off from time to time. I ain't never been one for shift work. I strictly on day time.

Made it clear to Mrs. Arnold and my other ladies; when time for me to pull off my apron, it coming off, and I gone. Oh, so you know Julius? He on his way to work, so he say. His job is hanging out with Pin Stripe over at the grill with all them other fellows. I done cook his goose, but he ain't gonna know 'bout it 'til he get home and gets to talking with Grace.

Nurse Preston, this place where we living is a big *town*; it ain't no big city, as you well know, and it don't do nobody no good to lie 'cause the truth gonna come out. I ain't never gonna lie to nobody. I minds my own business, and I is known to tell it like it is. That Julius just done tell me one of the biggest, black lies ever been told on this here bus. Here I is sitting in church a few Sundays ago, talking with his wife Grace like I is talking with you now.—Ain't you know Grace? I figure you do.—Anyhow, we sitting there waiting for the prayer meeting to get started, and I just happen to ask her 'bout the children, especially her boy Oscar.

Nurse Preston, Grace eyes done get full of tears just at the mention of her boy Oscar name. She blowing her nose hard to keep from crying. Then, she tell me Oscar ain't in the Army no more. He been in charge of the food store, the one they call the commissary store, where everybody with the identification card can get in to buy the food. Mind now, Oscar married, with four children Julius and Grace ain't never laid eyes on. Anyhow, Oscar got the girlfriend working the cash register where they check out the food. They up to date on them things 'cause they got what you call some kind of scanner. Anyhow, I know it make a little noise when things go over something on the counter. The girlfriend ringing up one thing and skipping every other meat package for certain people Oscar got in the Army for friends. Oscar and them friends get them meat package ain't been ring up and sell them to other people not in the Army. Oh yes, Nurse Preston. Grace say they done catch him good. They done one of them stakeout undercover watch on Oscar. They got all them other people, too, and they know exactly how long Oscar been doing that thing.

They done take Oscar stripes he had; plus, they take him to court. No, Grace say it ain't no court like you or me might get to go in. This court they call *martial*. What's that you say, Nurse Preston? Oh, it call *court martial*? That what it is then. They court martial Oscar, and he spend time in an army jail. Plus, they done *dishonor* him. Oh, excuse me. I must hear Grace wrong. You say the Army give Oscar a *dishonest discharge*? Well,

Nurse Preston, whatever they call it, Oscar done get it. Sure wish I could see Julius face when he tell Grace I done seen him and ask 'bout they boy Oscar. It just don't pay to lie, especially in this here town.

Nurse Preston, I saw your cousin Evalina the other day and, Lord, she still waiting for her girl Rebecca to come home. Her hair done turn white, what little left, and she sure got her hands full with keeping her momma. Those four little girls of Rebecca is sure some darlings. Lord knows that Evalina got a lot of faith. She keep telling everybody Rebecca still living. Ain't no way you gonna get a momma to believe her child dead, and she ain't seen no body.

Is this where you getting off? Well, enjoy your day 'cause over at that hospital it ain't easy with all the sickness and death.

Good morning, Brother Sanders. How Sister Sanders doing these days? No sir, can't rightly say I will. They got a program over at my church on that Sunday afternoon, and Reverend South counting on all his members being there when them other reverends come with their choir. Here, you take this. I gonna give you this little donation now to help you. No, keep the envelope. Just put this money in it. I know it gonna get to the right place. No, Brother Sanders, I speak the truth. It ain't no difference to me if they is women reverends. But none of them got no business talking 'bout "render to Caesar what belong to Caesar, and give to God what belong to God." I know everything come from God, and God give and God take away. I still say bless be the name of God.

I want your reverend to pay me back the money she done borrow from me before she got the calling she say she done get to preach. I telling you this 'cause I ain't gonna sit and hear her lying through the teeth, and she been holding my hard earn money for more than three years now. Reverend South does have a program that night, but I ain't gonna lie to you. I ain't been coming to your church to hear your lying reverend if I was not going to my church.

How many members in your church now? About seventeen, you say? Well, Brother Sanders, every time somebody gets mad in church, look out; they gonna start they own church. Ain't nothing wrong with that, I guess, but rather than follow some of these reverends, some of them same folks would have done better if they stand on a rock in the desert and slap a cross on top of the rock. If they got the faith and mean to love God from the heart and do the right thing, that same rock in the desert gonna grow. The church always gonna be. People come and people go, and the church still here. I don't always agree with what the Reverend South do, but as long as he read the exact words from the Bible, I gonna stay and listen. He flip the page in his big, old Bible, and I turning the pages in my little Bible. I follow every word he reading. I ain't doing what Reverend South say do, I doing what the Bible say do.

Brother Sanders, how long you and Sister Sanders been members in your other church? Fifty-six years. See, that's what I talking 'bout. That church of yours done had three reverends to serve you and Sister Sanders, and just 'cause the church ain't gonna buy him no new tires for his car, Satan done get in the midst and separate all them good folks who done grow up in that church, and they children, too, who got they own children in the Sunday school. Now, Brother Sanders, it be your business and not mine, but I sure would like to know how come that reverend can't buy them car tires from the pastor salary he been getting. Not enough salary he getting? How come he ain't living in the house the church done buy for that? His wife don't want to drive the distance to her job? Now, ain't that grand. I done hear everything now. Sure sound like your reverend need a job, Brother Sanders. Oh, he got one. I know that right. With seventeen members he better have a job.

Brother Sanders, be sure to tell Sister Sanders I done ask 'bout her. You take care riding this bus getting on and getting off. Now

Lord, it sure is a shame the way some folks let Satan just come in and tear everything up.

No, now it can't be. If it ain't Slappy Two. This old bus must be late for some good reason this day. Man, who ever think I gonna see you. Sit down, son. Slappy Two, ain't you looking good. If your daddy Slappy been living he sure would be proud of you.

Jerome might be your name, but you always gonna be Slappy Two to me and everybody knowing you. Don't worry 'bout that, son; everybody got something 'bout them they ain't wanting folks to know 'bout. That been the damnedest thing I ever hear. Ha ha ha ha ha. Lord, can anybody picture a cow with tennis shoes on? Your daddy Slappy done steal the cow, put tennis shoes on the cow backward, and walk that cow from the farm. Sure, people seen Slappy with the cow, but they just thinking Slappy touch in the head. Shucks, your daddy know exactly what he been doing. He done work on that farm the whole season, and then old man Gentile come telling him the crop bad and ain't nothing to share.

Slappy done walk that cow near to six miles in them tennis shoes, right to Mr. Lampson butcher shop. Sure we all know 'bout the cow, but ain't a soul say a word to the sheriff. Nobody like that damn sheriff, neither. That sheriff been so nasty to folks, the family been scared to tell in the paper where they done bury him.

Your daddy Slappy been a good man. Maybe he been a little feeble in the head 'cause everybody stop putting up with old man Gentile shit years ago, except your daddy. The way he stay up the road on that old, run down farm, we ain't never gonna be sure why he been satisfied with his lot.

Them tennis shoes sure fix that old sheriff. The tracks lead right to the farm 'cause the tennis been on the cow feet backward. That sheriff been dead. He dead in that grave ain't nobody know where it is still puzzle by that cow. Old man Gentile still living on that old farm look like it gonna fall in on him any day. Sure, that man got money. He ain't never pay nobody a good day's pay. He been taking and taking all his life, and now he ain't got nobody. Them neighbors he got don't look his side.

Your daddy Slappy ain't always been feeble in the head when he been young. That come from all them blows the police give to him. Things like that come about these days, ain't gonna be hush hush, like we done take it quiet in years back. I been living up the road then, and everybody know everybody living along that railroad track. Your daddy and me use to play and jump the train car shadows and wave at them porters working on the train. The trains always slow down when they near the crossing where we been living.

That been a terrible day that day. That train crash in that car, and them bodies been lying all over the crossing. Some people been hurt on the train. They say the people on the train in the dining car been the ones really hurt in a bad way. Everybody start running to the crossing when the train hit the car. Now, you take your daddy Slappy, he always did been a fast runner. I ain't sure if he been standing on the corner or where he come from, but all the folks say Slappy been the first one at that crossing. They had two ladies that had suppose to be in the car, but when that train hit that car, them bodies fly out that car. They say the clothes been tear off them ladies, and Slappy been just standing and looking.

Folks say Slappy been in shock. He see all that blood, and them ladies got body parts missing. Slappy ain't been in no shape to move. Them police been real bad back then. I hear say when they get to the crossing and see Slappy just standing there looking, they get them billy clubs and beat all over Slappy just 'cause he been looking at them dead ladies with hardly no clothes on. They beat poor Slappy down to the ground.

Your poor daddy been in shock from what he see; he ain't know if he been coming or going. The poor man could not move. He ain't never move a hand to keep them billy clubs from hitting him.

Hospital? If they take your daddy to a hospital, I ain't never hear 'bout that part. Sure, we all done see what happen. Ain't nobody stay in the house that day. Slappy ain't the only one been in shock; he just happen to be the black man standing near them dead white ladies. Old lady Laura come from her house with quilts, trying to cover up them bodies. Lord knows that been a mess that day.

When the word start getting 'round what done happen to Slappy, hell done break loose. All them folks on the train just moving around with no place to go. No sir, they ain't let the first black people off that train. They been told to stay on board. They done take Slappy, and the crossing loaded with police, doctors, and some mad ass black folks. Ain't been a thing nobody could do to stop them fellows from taking on them police that day. Them fellows from Ridge Hill, Smalls Corner, Moss Heights, and the Yellow Line all done come together.

Mind now, they all use to fight each other. Friday and Saturday nights been some razor cutting and shooting when they walk in a club and see them fellows inside from someplace else. They women been bad, too. Them women use them ice pick like them police use them billy club. They ain't getting you with the ice pick, they got you with the lye. They been known to mixing that lye with syrup. Many the times I see them running and screaming when I been up the road with Auntie. Pulling the skin off and screaming.

Them fellows don't play round with each other. They all done get joined together and, Slappy Two, them fellows cut some police ass that day. They done it fast like, and them ambulance drivers went on 'bout they business putting them hurt people in the ambulance and getting them off the crossing. Them fellows working the ambulance ain't say a thing. They been picking up them body parts like your daddy Slappy use to pick old man Gentile corn. Fast as them fellows lay them police out, them ambulance fellows haul them away.

No, not a white person on that train get hurt by them fellows. I know it been close to a hour of bloody fighting 'cause all the roads leading to the railroad crossing been block off, and the city bus been block off going back to the city on the other side of the train. That bus run on the hour, just like this damn late ass bus. All of us standing could see the other bus coming from the city a block off.

No, Slappy Two, not a soul been hurt on them buses, and in them cars, neither. Them fellows ain't been mad at them people. They been after the police. Them people been innocent. They ain't done a thing to your daddy Slappy.

When they beat up your daddy that day, they just done take the top off the boiling pot. All the hate just boil over from what them dirty police been doing for so long.

After them fellows get through, they disappear so fast. For a long time they had police cars driving up and down the road day and night. The police been asking everybody if they know who the fellows been. Everybody done know in the first place ain't gonna do no talking to the police. They ain't never say where they take your daddy. All everybody know is that Slappy ain't been round for a long time, and when Slappy show up, he act feeble in the head. Your daddy take a bad beating. He loose the job he had. That be the cause he work on old man Gentile farm. I know you don't know nothing 'bout no farm. That's one thing I'll say 'bout your momma Lillie Ruth, she done good by you.

I know all 'bout you playing football. You a fast runner, just like your daddy Slappy been. I hear tell you marry up with Ella Jane girl, Loretta. Sure, I remember Loretta. She always did know she been going places.

How long you say your car been in the garage? Over a week. Where the garage at you got the car in? Might be another week fore you get your car back. You ain't done hear what happen?

Elmore ain't working in the garage no more. I hear tell everything back up over there since Elmore gone.

How many children you and Loretta got? Three. I bet they some pretty children. All three boys. Guess I best say you got some handsome fellows to be proud of. How old the children now? Nine, eleven, and twelve. They know what done gone down with Slappy they granddaddy? What you waiting for? Slappy Two, I gonna say this now 'cause it should have been told to them boys when they been younger. Everybody you know ain't gonna mind they own business like I does. I always careful not to put my nose in other people business. Slappy Two, tell them boys 'bout your daddy Slappy 'cause, if you ain't gonna do it, somebody gonna tell them boys they granddaddy steal a cow and put tennis shoes on the cow. How you think that gonna sound on the ears of boys nine, eleven, and twelve? Ain't no need to set them boys up to heartbreak.

One thing 'bout riding this here bus, I gets to see folks I ain't seen in years. I too glad to see you this day. All us just passing through this old world. Sometimes we done hurt folks, and most times we done hurt ourself and too fool to take notice 'cause we full of pride. Your daddy Slappy been a good fellow, and I can't rightly say that he ever hurt anybody.

Hear tell you got the best ball team going now. How long you been the coach? That long, eh? What you mean how I know 'bout you coaching? I know this much, that coach they had fore you get there ain't been getting no kind of play from them fellows on the team. I know 'bout half of them parents stay home from the game 'cause you put Hester son Gilbert to call them plays. They ain't been liking having no black fellow back quarting. What you say? Oh, *quarter backing*. Well, whatever. I know the newspaper stop putting the game news on the front page of the sport section.

I hear Mr. Arnold tell Miss Arnold that, if they don't get parents to support the children, that school gonna be just like it once been.

It ain't the children; it been them parents. They ain't been no good example for them children. Children in school getting 'long good, all pulling together to make a good name for the school and this town, and here you got parents acting the fool 'cause changes done been made for the better. You done right to stick by your gun. For once, black parents show interest when Gilbert pass the ball; fore he been doing that, ain't hardly no black parents at them games. Then, when you play Gilbert, the white parents stop going to the games. That be just like I hear it be said: "You can please some of the people some of the time, but you can't please all the people all the time."

So, Slappy Two, I hear tell you start flipping the coin at the start of the game and you let Gilbert and that white fellow call the coin. That been a real smart move. Black and white done pay to see the game 'cause they ain't knowing who gonna pass the ball. Hear tell you been offered a contract at some colleges. Everybody want you now.

How your momma-in-law Ella Jane doing? It been over thirty years since I last seen her. After your daddy-in-law Robert die, she gone to live with her sister in East Orange.

Somebody did say she had *sugar* and lose a leg. Glad to know she still living. Some people just give up. Tell your momma Lillie Ruth hello for me. It be a blessing, Lillie Ruth with you and Loretta in the house. With her eye sight getting weak, she bless to have a son like you. It don't take some folks a second thought to throw old folks in a home these days. Our folks use to care for our people. No matter how low and sick people get back then, we ain't never been known to put them in no home. Ain't had to be no blood kin, either. We call everybody uncle and auntie who take us in young and take care of us back then. Now, all we been hearing is family value. We always did been having it. That is 'til lately, for some folks. Course now, we always did have the church

94

upbringing and trying to do everything to hold the family togeth-er. Shucks, we just been thanking God and making it day to day. Ain't nobody been putting no name like family value to it.

This here your stop? Take it easy, Slappy Two. Ha ha ha ha ha. Okay, *Jerome*. I know you ain't wanting your ball team calling you Coach Slappy Two. I gonna keep up with your movement, son.

Good morning. Sure, sit on down. The fool got eyes and can see you pregnant. He ain't got no manners this morning. He could wait 'til you sit down before jerking this bus on.

You feeling better today? You ain't been feeling too hot Friday gone. How far gone you is? Five months. I thought so 'cause you got the swelling in the feet. You gonna get a little swelling. One thing I glad 'bout, you ain't smoking no more. Last month, just fore you get on the bus, I see through the window you putting out the cigarette. Smoking ain't no good for you, even worse now you pregnant.

Things alright on the job? Honey, that just goes to show you what a education good for. First you been the typing clerk, now you on them computers. A sit down job better for you with you being pregnant. My friend Veronica stand on her feet for hours working in the mall store. The Lord done put you in a job to keep you off them swell up feet while you carrying the baby.

Hold on, honey, He ain't right in the head this morning. He a asshole for sure, but I ain't letting him 'cause me to lose my religion.

Veronica feet giving her trouble, and she ain't pregnant. Hers come from standing on them concrete floor long hours over the years. I see them there boots you got on 'cause it cold, and it gonna get colder. You need to get out of them boots at work. You best take you some support shoes in for work. Oh, you got some at work? That's good, then. You plan to work after the baby come? Honey, that be the best thing to do. When you going to your husband? Next month? I know your momma gonna miss you. But you doing the right thing. Married folks need to be together. Specially them your age. How long you say he been in the Navy? Seven years? That sound like he like it. You got sense, you be every place he got the duty on shore. Oh, *shore duty* you say it is.

Sure gonna miss having you on this here bus. I just been thinking that, if you had tell your brother *no* when he ask to borrow your car, you and me never know each other. He done tear up your car, hurt in the hospital, and now you riding the bus for the last three months. I hear tell that been a real bad accident. No, he ain't lucky; he blessed. They got some good people that help people like your brother Joe. Your brother Joe is young, and given time with a lot of prayers, he gonna be up on his feet again.

How many times he got to go in the theory room at the hospital? Oh, he be in *therapy*. Well, how many times he in that room? Three times a week. I bet he got a good insurance. Lord knows the way things is these here days, high prices done gone up everywhere.

Oh, this ain't your first born you carrying now? How old the other one is? Four. That don't make no never mind if your husband ain't the first one daddy. He gonna put his name on the papers for your first one? He already done it? That's good. Now, he really sound like a good man you done get. How some of these women done put they own children aside, talking 'bout the man say he ain't taking care of another man's child, sounds crazy to me. Honey, it be me and he talk fool talk like that, I tell him mighty damn quick, "You love me, love my children." Ain't no way under God's sun I put my children on the side for these things wearing britches calling theyself man.

How you meet such a fine man? At the hair salon. Which one? No, I was told that they real nice in there, and make you feel important. They introduce everybody, and they ain't eating and smoking all over the place. Yeah, that true, too, 'cause Clyde sister that work for Mr. Baron tell me that she call one day to get her hair fix, and the girl been real nice on the phone and tell her thanks for calling and she looking forward to having her come in. So your husband been with his friend off the ship to pick up his wife, and you been in the salon waiting for your sister Flora. He friend wife Nancy been talking with your sister Flora, and when them fellows come in, he spot you right away. You all leave together and gone to the club on the base.

Ain't it strange how things work out for some folks. You just been in the right place at the right time. Blessings sure come in different ways. I sure hope and pray everything gonna turn out good for you and your little ones. You mean about the 'doption? Yeah, you right; I mean a-doption. Better for you to tell than have somebody else tell. Some people just don't know how to mind they own business. I ain't never been able to figure out how come some people so nosy. Ain't like me to mind folks business. I always been pleasant with everybody, and I guess folks just take a liking to me. Ain't never hurt me nor nobody else in the good sense to take time to speak to people. I try to help folks out from time to time, just pointing out little things they too busy to notice.

Anyways, now I telling you this, but I ain't calling no names. Been 'bout maybe four winters back and I ain't really been sick, but my throat been hurting me that Sunday, and I know I ain't been in no voice to sing. That been my choir time to sing that Sunday. Anyways, just like I been saying, I ain't sitting in the choir due to my throat. I don't let little things stop me from going to church and to my job. I always did put the Lord first, and he gives me the jobs second, so I ain't worrying 'bout a thing. I sitting behind maybe the seven row in church—'cause Reverend South got all them mike things hook up, and it can get right loud when the spirit done hit him. Everybody just praising the Lord and thankful for just being alive.

Well, honey, this here lady sitting right in front of me got on a pretty piece of fur round the neck I ever done see. It been the real thing; ain't been no fake 'cause it look pretty and soft and just flutter up when she move, and Miss Arnold I works for got one, and it soft and pretty like that one. I done feel Miss Arnold one and it feel good. Well now, this lady wearing her hair in one of them curls. *Jerri curl?* Honey, I don't know one from the other; all I know is the hair curl and got all this stuff just dripping down on that pretty fur. No, I ain't notice nothing 'til the spirit done hit her, and she start to moving to the music. Oh, she been one happy soul.

We all shouting and having a good time. I done reach over and yank Marcella wig back on the head 'cause it done twist all 'round. See, I been telling Marcella, them hats she got ain't fitting over them wigs she wearing. Every Sunday she coming to church looking like she got on *two* hats. That's besides the point. If she gonna wear wigs, she ought to have sense to stop buying them big things. Some of them other folks in the church hair ain't all that long, but they got them fancy looking cuts, and they sure as hell look good. Marcella come telling me folks done use to her wearing them wigs, and she might look funny to them without the wigs. Shit, she look funny to me with them wigs on under them big hats.

Anyhow, like I been saying, all of the white stuff dripping down on this lady fur piece 'round the neck, and it so pretty. I just lean over when she get through shouting and say low, quiet like, "Sister, your hair is dripping something white on your fur."

Honey, she swing 'round so fast to look at me, whatever been dripping from her hair done splash up in my face. No, she ain't say thank you. She been in a piss mood. I ain't never seen nobody lose religion like that sister. She tell me, "It ain't nothing but mink, and if the mink can stand the curl keeper, other people need to mind they own business and look at the reverend, and not what people got on the hair. And besides, you need to mind your own business."

98

Now, I done get pissed, and they done start another song. Everybody thinking the spirit done hit me when I reach out. But you see, when that bitch swing that head of hers 'round again and that stuff she call curl keeper done fling on my face again and spots done get on my white wool suit I done had in lay-a-way for six months, I took to the floor straight out of my seat, and I had a hand of hair from that head holding, shoving, and pulling. I been just a-yelling and everybody thinking the spirit done touch me, and that sister bitch screaming 'cause I beating the shit out of her. I hold on a long time 'cause, Marcella tell me later, they done catch hell getting my hold loose.

One good thing, everybody gonna know for sure how Marcella look without them wigs 'cause, in the shaking me loose, Marcella wig done come *off*. That ain't all done happen. Sister Bitch curls ain't been all *her* curls. Weave! That's what it been, a *weave*. Sure, I know what I talking 'bout 'cause I had the whole piece of weft in my hand. Well, at the time I ain't been knowing what no weft been. Marcella tell me.

Thread? No, ain't no thread been on that thing. It been some glue. The glue been black. Whoever put that weave on sure know what they been doing 'cause it look just like Sister Bitch hair.

How come I call her Sister Bitch? Well, when I been trying to be nice and call her *sister*, she put her ass on her shoulder and act piss off with me. She ain't had no right to sound me off like that; I was just concern 'bout the greasy stuff dripping on the fur. So, since she sound like an asshole, she Sister *Bitch* to me.

The brothers and Marcella done pull me away. Next thing I know they done had me in the toilet room. No, I ain't never seen that bitch before. She must a been a visitor. She ain't been back neither.

Why you laughing? Age? What my age got to do with it? I been mad as hell. I ain't got much, but my few pieces of clothes is quality.

I ain't lying when I say it take me six months on lay-a-way to get that suit. I see little dots in it now from that stuff from them curls. Who? Reverend South? Far as I know he ain't never miss a beat in the preaching and shouting. He up there in the pulpit and we down in the pews fighting, and he thinking we full of the Holy Ghost. Some strange things go on in churches.

Well, here you is. Be careful walking 'cause them sidewalks got holes full with water. You don't want to step in one, accident like.

Good morning, Lottie Mae. How things going with you, lady? I know that's right. I plan to be right there. They done promise to pick me up round 'bout four thirty on that morning. We gonna go in a van Rose oldest girl, Debbie, gonna rent. Why I going to Rose graduation? I guess you ain't notice that young girl that just get off this here bus. Well, I ain't one to talk 'bout nobody business, but I proud of that girl and all them others that done get up off the dirt. But it ain't no thanks to some folks I knows that tries to keep 'em down for life.

No, now, you wait a minute; you done ask, and now I gonna tell you. All us know Rose got her four children, and she been down, down low as any soul gonna get. She ain't never been married. No, she ain't. I don't care what you say, Lottie Mae. I know for a fact that man ain't been free to marry Rose 'cause when Rose gone to the base to check why she ain't been getting one of them 'lottment checks, like all of her friends who done marry up with them service fellows, that been when Rose find out she ain't been the wife.

Well, then it is a-llotment check; she still ain't been getting it, whatever they call it. No, she ain't leave him then. She been so crazy 'bout that man. She fall for all them lies he done tell her. She going 'round telling folks they done got the payroll mess up and they waiting for the divorce papers to get to payroll, and he gonna just give her the money 'til they get it straight in Washington. Four children Rose had for that man. What his name been? Yep, they call him Chicago, but I ain't never know the real name. He ain't been born in no Chicago; that sucker been from Mississippi. Been better for Rose if he stay where he been from. He come home one day, course now, it ain't been his home 'cause Rose been living in that house since her momma die 'bout seven or eight years after Rose daddy, Brother Nelson, pass. Rose been doing fine, going to church, had a good job, clear mortgage house to live in, and just ripe for a no account like that Chicago fellow to sucker in.

I ain't getting into how they done meet 'cause, like I trying to tell you, that ain't my business. First, Rose done tell everybody she marry. Next thing, Rose got one baby, two baby, three baby, and now, four grown children. Anyway, he gone home to Rose house and tell her he got some emergency orders to transfer, and he gonna send for her and the children soon as he get settle in. Even tell Rose he had secret orders, and nobody was to know where he gonna be. Shit, that been twenty-three years ago.

Rose had a hard time. Let me tell you, it ain't been easy for Rose. Them some sweet children Rose got, and every one done finish school. I knows the time Rose ain't had no money. I knows the time Rose ain't had no food and no heat in the house. I knows the time when Rose and me done talk and pray, and now I see how God done answer prayers.

Lottie Mae, you just like so many of them others on this here bus. You ain't got the eye to see the goodness in folks. I know all 'bout how your children ain't had nothing to do with Rose children over at the schoolhouse. And, I believe to my soul, that it all done gone back to you 'cause of your children treating Rose children like they done. You done reap what you say through your mouth all 'bout other folks and they children. You so quick to point the finger at Rose, 'cause she make them mistakes, and yet every one of the children Rose done bring in this world doing damn good.

No, don't try to stop me. I ain't finish yet. Rose children good role models. People change, and I just pray that one day you live long enough to see your children change. No, I ain't getting into your children failures 'cause that gonna be another subject. Right now, I getting you straight on Rose.

For the past seven years, Rose been going back to school, and I happy to tell you now, she gonna walk taller and march up to the president of that college and get that paper that gonna tell everybody Rose ain't down no more. I been with Rose every step of the way. Ain't been just me; others been praying and helping, too. I too glad for Rose. Oh, you the main one done the talking, and I ain't scared to tell you to the face right here and now. It been the lie when you talk 'bout Rose coming home one o'clock at night 'cause she been running 'round. Rose been running up and down that highway going to classes at that college three years straight, and then driving up during the summer for almost four years. When Rose car done clunk out on her, she come to me. What could I do? I gone straight to the bank with Rose and tell that lady down there in the bank I work for Miss Arnold, and how long I been working for Miss Arnold. The lady ask me if she could call Miss Arnold. I tell her go right on and call. I sign the papers, and Rose had the money she need to put the stomach part right in the car. Well, you call it *engine*, the *motor*, or whatever, but it sure been what Rose need. You start the lie 'cause you see my nephew Greg put Rose car to run again right in Rose yard. You say Greg been Rose boyfriend. Oh, yes, you *did* do it. I the one call Greg wife Letha and tell her myself I done send Greg to Rose house to fix the car.

See, all of this you ain't know nothing 'bout. A devil always stay busy, and you been in the middle of his workings. But I tell you now, Lottie Mae; God ain't dead, and He see all. All the time you been busy spreading lies 'bout Rose and trying to keep her down, the Lord been steady fixing a sure way for her to get out of the miry clay. I gonna tell Rose 'bout a song I done hear when I been real little, and that song done stick with me. The song say, "Hurry, sundown, see what tomorrow bring. It may bring sunshine, and it may bring rain."

I gonna just lie back in that van and let the sun soak through the windows 'cause I got the feeling it ain't gonna rain one drop when Rose get that college degree. It sure ain't no secret what God can do. You ain't been in church last Sunday 'cause, if you been, you would know that Reverend South done read the graduation invitation from Rose and a letter from her thanking me and my nephew Greg and some other folks for helping her out during, what she call, a "most turbulent time" of her life.

I say to myself, go on, Rose; sock it to them with your college word. You of all people ought to been there 'cause all the sisters that belong to your lying circle been in church too shock to say a word. Course now, Reverend South ain't had let the secretary read the invitation and letter from Rose. Reverend South know well what he been doing to read the letter hisself. Now, you done hear it all from me why I get to go to Rose graduation.

Hard feelings? Toward who? You? No, Lottie Mae, people like you always gonna be 'round. I gonna be friendly with you 'cause I ain't gonna let death come to me and catch me mad at nobody. Hard things I just take to the Lord and leave it there. Tell myself that God will understand and say, well done.

Where you on your way today? I thought you tell me your son Lester want you to stop work and move in with him. Lester forgot he got a wife? I know that's right. What the real estate man say when you tell you change your mind? I guess not. He done lose out on a sale. What about the car Lester promise you? The last time I see Lester, he pick you up at church when it rain so bad that time, and he been talking loud saying he gonna get his momma a car so she won't have to ride no public bus no more.

Well, Lottie Mae, this public bus still carrying you. What happen to the car? Oh, I see. Lester wife Shondell say she need a new car and let their son Vernon have Shondell car.

It be that way sometime. Sometimes it best things happen to us fore we make a move, 'cause most times we find out all moves ain't for the best. Ain't you remember Sister Erma? You ain't been in the church then? Yes you is been in the church then 'cause she been the mother of the church when you and Rubin get married. Sure, she been old then. She been over a hundred when she die. She outlive every one of her children and a few of her grands. You remember when the twin boys been coming home from New York for Thanksgiving, and they had that bad accident with all them cars on the expressway? Well, the twins get kill, and when the momma hear what happen, she had the stroke and been down since. 'Til the day she die, she ain't never say another word after she done say, "Lord, have mercy," when the call come on the phone 'bout her twin boys.

No, I don't know where I been, but I ain't been there when they call and tell the twins been dead. I been told that's what the momma say. Anyhow, like I been saying, Sister Erma been old and all her children dead, and it been just her living in that old big house. Don't get me wrong now. Lottie Mae, ain't been nothing wrong with the house, but it been a upstairs house and with Sister Erma being so old and everything else, steps ain't been a part of the everyday living for her no more.

She first gone to live with her great grandson Walter. She crying in church that Walter lock her up in one room. Next thing we know, Walter done put Sister Erma back to her house. Then, Walter brother, Scott, come from somewhere up north—we ain't figure out where—but later on another fellow done move in the house with Scott. And let me tell you, that been more than meet the eye, if you know what I mean.

104

Lottie Mae, when Walter and them three sisters and them two grand aunts and uncle done figure out what been going on, they done get over to Sister Irma house. They done stick to they gun and tell Scott to get away from that house and take the friend with him. Scott tell them he need time to get hisself together, and he be gone by the weekend, but more than he been gone by the week-end. Sister Irma had some of that heavy, old furniture with them four post bed. That no account Scott pull out in the middle of the night and take just 'bout all he want of all that pretty furniture.

Now, that ain't all that done gone wrong. Two weeks after that no account Scott leave, papers done come saying the house up for sale. Poor Walter almost lose his mind when he done find out Scott done somehow get Sister Irma to sign the house over to him. When Sister Irma been young, she start working for lawyer Benson when he first start what they call *read the law*. When lawyer Benson son get marry, Sister Irma gone to his house and carry right on with work. I know good and well Sister Irma put in all her work years with that one family. Walter use his head now. He ain't forgetting how crazy that Benson family been 'bout Sister Irma. Sister Irma been too old to work and they still been giving her money every week.

What you mean, how come I know so much? See, Lottie Mae, just like I been trying to tell you, you ain't never gonna learn nothing 'cause you ain't gonna keep your mouth shut. Ain't you know you can't talk and hear at the same time. Like I been trying to say, Walter done call young lawyer Benson and done demon-strate against them papers Scott done say Sister Irma sign. If it ain't *demonstrate*, what they call it? *Contest, protest*, whatever they call it, lawyer Benson done put a stop to it, and Scott had to haul every piece of furniture back to the house.

Who, Scott? Ain't nobody seen him in town. All I know is the truck driver and a man been with him haul the furniture back in the house. Lawyer Benson say Scott get Sister Irma to sign them papers 'cause she ain't been knowing what she sign, and them papers ain't had no witness name to say Sister Irma sign on the line. Scott been told he pressure Sister Irma to sign them papers under duress.

I ask the same thing 'cause I ain't never hear nothing 'bout no duress. Mrs. Arnold tell me that mean Scott threaten Sister Irma, and she been too old and scared to say a thing. Anyhow, Walter daughter stay in the house with Sister Irma, and Sister Irma die in she own house.

I ain't signing what little I got to nobody. With the help of the good Lord, I providing for just what I need. Insurance? Listen, Lottie Mae, if they ain't got enough to buy me with what I paying, that the children problem. It ain't gonna be my problem. I gonna be dead. It ain't gonna make no difference to me. Why put all that money in the ground trying to outdo the last funeral, when the living can use the money. It ain't right for a family to pay on a funeral when the body been in the ground for over a year or more.

Girl, don't start me. You damn well know what I talking 'bout. See, that's another thing. Them children live out of town, ain't got a penny, but they come home and pick out the most expensive casket. They conscience killing them, that what it is. They ain't done a thing for people while they living; now, the people dead, and they want to look big. How come they don't use that money when them people sick and need it. I hates all them damn flowers. Can't even see how the casket look with all them damn flowers all over it.

Then, another thing, how come we got to hold dead people so long? What you mean give people time to get home? Lottie Mae, I done tell my children, them that's here and them that ain't here, if they ain't here the third day I done gone to meet the Lord, ain't no need for them to come, 'cause I will be in the ground. That ain't my fault they ain't got the money to get home. And if somebody else in my family done gone and die, ain't no use for them to look for me to send money to get them back down here for nobody funeral. They grown and know they got folks down here. They best put money aside for death, 'cause death sure is gonna come. Death is that uninvited guest that gonna come visit every house.

You done pick out your casket? Good for you. I ain't picking out no casket for me; I can care less. Ain't I done tell you it ain't gonna make no difference to me? I got my family straight on just one thing. I done walk in that church in Sunday school. I done grow up in there. I done get married in that church. I done get divorce, and I still in that church. I sing in that church choir, and I gonna get buried out of that church. I even fight in church, and Reverend South think I been shouting 'cause of the Holy Spirit. God done forgive me for that. Ha ha ha ha ha.

I almost itching for that fool bus driver to do like the school children say, "come all unglue." The way I feel now, I'll scotch tape his ass real good. That ain't true. More people need to be like me. I always tell people just what I thinking. It ain't gonna do me no good to tell somebody else 'bout what wrong with you. If I do that, it ain't gonna help you at all 'cause you the problem. So I just as well tell you; that way ain't nobody adding or taking away a thing I got to say. Now, Lottie Mae, if I lying you tell me.

You mean Laura? Now, I done hear everything. If she cry, she had a right to cry. She know she been wrong. I get off work from Miss Arnold early that day 'cause I had that appointment with the doctor for three fifteen. I give the nurse Miss Arnold number to call if the doctor change my appointment time. Well, when I get to the doctor office, who sitting in there? It been Laura husband Anthony, and he say he come to pick up Laura. We been talking while I been waiting for my appointment call. Laura come in, and all three of us been talking. Then, the nurse say *next*, and Laura get up to go in the doctor room. I say, "Wait a minute, Laura. I been here first. I next, and not you."

She tell me that the nurse always put her in the doctor room right away when she come in. I say to her, "That may be alright on them other days, but my appointment time say three fifteen and it way pass that time. And if *next* mean *next* like I know *next* mean, then *I* the next one going in that doctor room."

Laura look me up and down and say the doctor seem to be in the practice of treating *anybody* with a little insurance cover. You see, Lottie Mae, the way Laura say *anybody* kind of move me out of the path of righteousness into the body of temptation. Girl, I razz her up one side and down the other. I take her back when all us had the same outhouse. It been five family living in that court. Laura family and my family been the last ones to move out of that court. All us share that same one outhouse toilet. Now, she a school secretary, and I still working my day work. I does respectable work and I proud of what I do, and I ain't letting nobody look down on me.

Anthony? Lottie Mae, Anthony ain't open his mouth 'cause he know I been right. Ain't I tell you it been five family living in that court? Anthony family been one of the five. That the big reason Anthony keep his mouth shut. He know he been catch by Mr. Heyward peeking in the half moon cut out at the top of the outhouse toilet, and Anthony momma Miss Millie cut his tail real good right in front of everybody.

All us been just like sisters and brothers growing up in that court. It ain't been nothing for me to sit down at Anthony momma table to eat, 'cause Anthony sit at my momma table or anybody else table in the court to eat. Who? Anthony daddy? Lottie Mae, don't ask me 'bout no daddy for Anthony. I ain't never seen no man in Miss Nellie house. All I seen was them children with Anthony, and all us ain't knowing if a man suppose to be in that house back then.

Anyways, like I been telling you 'bout high and mighty Miss Laura, she come asking Anthony if he gonna let me talk to her like I been doing. All Anthony say was I been next. Laura done lie if she say I done curse her out. She been crying like she been crying 'cause she know I is her conscience, and it don't make no difference to me if I been the secretary and she be the one work for Miss Arnold. That still ain't gonna change the fact that all us been poor in the same court. Every time she see me, and no matter where I be, just seeing me always gonna remind her that we is from the same place. I ain't one to forget where I done come from.

What you mean, then what happen? I goes on by Laura in the doctor room to see the doctor 'cause I been next. What I see the doctor for ain't your business, Lottie Mae.

Corrine? She been in love so much with Roger she done lose herself. I done give up even talking to her. I telling her 'bout what a good time the choir had singing up the country, she steady talking on 'bout Roger. I done get fed up with that, and I just come out and tell her I ain't got no mind to hear 'bout Roger *this* and Roger *that*. Hurt her feelings? Must not, 'cause she don't talk 'bout nothing else. Corrine been going down to visit Roger sister in Florida, but she ain't never been to Arkansas. Roger the one been going to Arkansas. All them time Roger been telling her his momma sick and he got to go home. Somehow, Corrine done scrape up the money to get Roger home to see his sick momma every time. All the time she thinking he down there with his momma and to see his aunts, uncles, and all them other relations he been telling her 'bout, but ain't never take her to meet. Sure, it hurt her real bad. When the momma ain't been sick, the aunts sick, the uncles sick, or some other folks in the family sick.

No, Roger sister in Florida ain't never say a thing to Corrine. I hear later that the sister ain't been back to Arkansas since she leave. No, Corrine and Roger ain't got no children. Corrine been trying to do good by all them nieces and nephews down there she ain't never seen. You know, like sending boxes of things from time to time. No, she ain't been knowing what she been getting into.

She gone home from work, and Roger done leave the message telling her his sister done die and he on the way to Arkansas. Well, girl, Corrine take off from work to get to the funeral for Roger sister, 'cause she say Roger need her at a time like that. That been when Corrine find out what been down all them years. Sure, I blame Corrine. You mean to tell me you been sleeping with a man all them years, he blowing his breath in your face, and you the wife ain't never been to his hometown, or wherever it is the momma staying if the momma still living?

Wait a minute now. Let me tell you what done been tell to me. Girl, I been too outdone when Corrine tell me she call Roger momma house, and when Roger come on the phone, she tell Roger where she been. Say Roger ask her what in the hell she doing there. Say Roger ask her if she call Agnes.—Agnes is the sister to Roger living in Florida that ain't been back to Arkansas.—Don't ask me *why* now, 'cause Corrine ain't been getting into that with me. Anyhow, Corrine tell Roger, no she ain't think to call Agnes 'cause she figure Agnes gonna be in Arkansas at the funeral. Why? Ain't I just tell you Corrine ain't telling me nothing 'bout them family problems. Anyhow, Roger gone and pick up Corrine and take her straight to a motel 'cause it ain't been no place for her to stay at the momma house. Corrine tell me she ain't seen Roger again 'til at the funeral the next day. He tell her to call a taxi to take her to the church 'cause he busy making sure all the family getting to the house to leave on time when the undertaker get to the house.

Wake? Lottie Mae, you still ain't hearing what I saying. Ain't I just tell you Corrine ain't seen Roger again 'til at the funeral? Corrine ain't been at no wake 'cause Roger ain't been to pick her up to take her to no wake. Now, how I suppose to know that? I been too outdone when Corrine tell me Roger ain't come to get her to sit with the family. It been just like she ain't been there. She in the church at a funeral and ain't knowing the first person in the whole church.

They done finish with the funeral and in the graveyard, when there was a lot of folks around, grown people, must have been 'bout twenty, twenty-two, or twenty-five keep looking at her in the graveyard. She know they ain't been under twenty years old, if they been a day under. Anyhow, all three done gone over to Corrine and tell Corrine they Roger children, and ask if she they Aunt Agnes. Girl, Corrine say she done look at them children like she crazy 'cause her head pounding with the blood, and she ain't been able to say a word.

That thing done something to Corrine head 'cause she ain't been the same since. She still got Roger on the brain 'cause she all the time talking 'bout him. I hear tell that Corrine uncle, Mr. Amos, gone to get Corrine and fly her back home. Roger ain't been from shit. All them times, he been going to Arkansas to his other wife and children. The other wife been satisfied 'cause Roger been getting home often and sending money. Oh, sure, he come to town to do the construction work with the new express-way, and so say marry up with Corrine. Them fellows down at the grill say Mr. Amos kill Roger for sure if he know what been done to Corrine fore he gone to Arkansas to check up on her, 'cause folks know Mr. Amos is known for packing a gun. Mr. Amos think the sun rise and set on Corrine 'cause Corrine momma been Mr. Amos only sister child, and everybody know Mr. Amos loved that sister. They must have been 'bout fifteen years apart, and Mr. Amos sure enough did look after his baby sister Lorraine. He tell everybody Corrine look just like her momma Lorraine.

No, 'cause Miss Lorraine die when Corrine been 'bout six years old. No, we ain't never know for sure. Them old folks just talk that Corrine come down with a high fever, and that been all she wrote. She die quick like. Roger ain't been back this side, and as for them children and Roger other wife, Mr. Amos ain't said hair nor hide 'bout them.

He ain't hold back on no money when it come to Corrine. He done had her back home by airplane, and the ambulance with Mr. Amos doctor inside pick up Corrine and take her straight to the hospital. Who? Mr. Amos? No way. Mr. Amos tell you up front he ain't flying in no airplane. He drive to Arkansas in that old Ford car he been having most all the years I been knowing him, and that car take off to bring him back when he make sure Corrine on that airplane. I telling you this, and Mr. Amos know it. But he ain't gonna accept it. Corrine ain't never gonna be the same in the head. All she talk 'bout is Roger, just like they still living together. Corrine been getting on this same bus talking 'bout Roger to anybody crazy enough to listen.

I hear tell Corrine ride the full route of this bus 'til it get right back where she get on; then, she get off. The next day she show back up and get right back on this here bus and ride the route again, telling folks 'bout Roger, just like clockwork.

Lottie Mae, I been doing some thinking. I thinking 'bout how all these here folks been riding this bus all these years just friendly like an old clock working. Not all been friendly now, but most been. I does get a little to feeling on the sad side when one of us ain't on here no more 'cause death done it again. So much happiness done happen to some of these same folks, and some sad times, too. Some of us been pulling up on this bus a long time, trying to get children through school, taking on more days to pay for college, and then them weddings. I just feel proud when I see the look on most faces 'cause I can tell you something good or bad 'bout everybody on this here bus. Don't get me wrong now, I ain't one to dwell on nobody misery 'cause I done had enough of that my own self.

For all I know this could well be my last day riding this bus, the way that old, fool ass driver turning the wheel and jerking off. He so mad at me, the fool don't even stop to think he can kill hisself and other folks on this bus. Don't pay him no mind he been driving fool when I first get on this bus. Drugs? No, now, I ain't saying he driving like he on some drugs. He driving like he plain fool. I done tell him all I had a mind to do 'cause, the good Lord willing, I be sitting right here on tomorrow. And if I ain't, then my time done come.

I call to mind when Essie Mae and I gone to a wake one night when I been in New York. Girl, it been cold that night. Who? No, I just been to keep Essie Mae company 'cause she ain't been wanting to be out by her lone self. No, I didn't know that dead body. That been Essie Mae friend on another side. What you mean? Just 'cause I been Essie Mae friend, that don't mean I gots to know her other friends. Anyway, Lottie Mae, you gonna let me get through telling you what happen that night or not? Well then, listen to what I trying to say.

We done gone to the funeral parlor for a wake. When we get there everybody just hanging on each other and patting each other with the crying and calling everybody cousin. No, we ain't been having no black dress on, the coats we had on just happen to be black. I had on a nice, black, wool scarf like one of them shawls on my head 'cause it been real cold. Next thing I know, somebody done grab me, calling me *cousin,* and crying all over me. I done look over for Essie Mae, and one of them big brothers of a cousin done grab a bear hold on Essie Mae. Everybody done take us for cousins, and the way they been carrying on, Essie Mae and me ain't said a thing. They done take me all over the parlor, telling folks I be a cousin. They done the same thing with Essie Mae. We been there almost a hour when Essie Mae and me done get together in the hall, and Essie Mae come telling me we had to get out of that funeral parlor in a hurry. The only thing I see wrong is that I tell Essie Mae them folks thinking I be they cousin. Essie Mae tell me that ain't all done happen. Essie Mae tell me she ain't never seen that dead man in the casket in her life before. We been at the wrong wake. Cold as the dickens in New York, and we at the wrong wake.

We done gone from that wake and end up at another wake, where Essie Mae see some folks she know. She come telling the folks I be her best friend. We stay 'til everybody leaving, and that when this fellow everybody been calling *Little Al* invite all us to what they call a wake party. Now, being from down here, I ain't never hear of such a thing as a wake party.

Anyhow, we all been at the wake, when Essie Mae come telling me we in the wrong place again 'cause the body we been trying to find for the wake gonna be put out the next night. I tell Essie Mae if she think I going all over New York freezing my ass off in the cold trying to find a dead body again, her head mess up for sure. What I decide to do? I stay right there and party all night long, just like everybody else. Feel guilty? What I had to feel guilty for? I ain't had know them dead people, and besides, we done all we been expect to do. We done pay our respect, even if we done respect the dead we ain't been knowing.

Girl, some crazy, fool things done happen to me in life. I remember one time we been up the country at a funeral, and it been real cold. I been real young, 'bout maybe ten or eleven. That wind been blowing so hard, and let me tell you, New York cold in the winter time, but it ain't like no cold down south in a country graveyard up on a hill, no trees and that old wind blowing.

You know how some folks leave from down south and go up north, and when they come back down home, they done get into this old act like they be fine and above they southern relations.

Well, honey, every time Lucy Mae come home, she all dress up fine in them pretty clothes and fur coat, with them hat matching the coat. I think I been most ten years old, and I always did like to be near Cousin Lucy Mae 'cause them fur coats been so pretty. Cousin Lucy Mae fur coat been the first real fur I done feel 'til I get grown up and start working for Miss Arnold. It been so cold in the graveyard most of the family just sitting in the undertaker family car. No, Lottie Mae; I say *car*. I seen one car, and I can remember it been one *family* car.

See now, that another thing we use to do back then. We ain't never had to get all them undertaker family cars 'cause folks always been willing to drive they car for the dead people family. Back then, we know just what good friends be, and besides, where we been gonna get the money for all them undertaker family cars? We had all the folks come to the funeral 'cause, then, most all funerals be on Saturday. You die this Saturday, you bury next Saturday or Sunday. Family been living all over. Half had no money to get home; most had to travel by the bus. Anyhow, it been so cold, some of us been standing in a group, and natural like Cousin Lucy Mae been the big shot.

Somebody been trying to get Cousin Lucy Mae to leave the group to get closer to the grave. Everybody then start to move up on the hill to the grave, and all of a sudden, Cousin Lucy Mae done trip and fall. We done turn around to see if Cousin Lucy Mae done trip on some vine. Girl, with that fine fur coat on, Cousin Lucy Mae bloomers with big and little holes done fall down to Cousin Lucy Mae shoes and done trip her face down in the graveyard.

Laugh? You think I been fool. What happen? My oldest sister Lillie get by Cousin Lucy Mae real fast like and throw her coat over Cousin Lucy Mae. Ha ha ha ha ha. I ain't been laughing then, but I done laugh many a time after, when I see in my mind how Cousin Lucy Mae look pulling and twisting trying to get

115

them bloomers up, and Lillie whispering, "Cousin Lucy Mae, take 'em off. Hurry up, Cousin Lucy Mae; take 'em off."

Cousin Lucy Mae get them bloomers off, wrap 'em 'round her hand, pretend she crying in sorrow, and use them bloomers like a handkerchief wiping her face. She had on this big, pretty, fur coat, but I know her ass been cold that day.

I don't know who see them bloomers 'round Cousin Lucy Mae shoes that day, but I know one thing, after that day my sister Lillie and me always did get a big box for Christmas from Cousin Lucy Mae. She even give Lillie one of them Parker pen set when Lillie finish grade school. Girl, during that time, getting a Parker pen set been a big thing to get. Cousin Lucy Mae always plop right at our house after that happen, all before she been staying uptown.

No, they been her first cousins. First, second, third; that ain't been no different. Shucks, we call folks cousin then who ain't been blood kin. Lottie Mae, you got some folks in your family the same way. Sure I know. Wallace Lee been Rachel Ann son, and you know he ain't been no cousin from up the country. Rachel Ann had Wallace Lee, and you know it well as I know it. That don't make no never mind now; it done happen 'cause your cousin Wallace Lee sure is here, and damn if he ain't a good looking man. Course now, it ain't my business if Rachel Ann going 'round telling folks she Wallace Lee auntie and ain't claiming that fine fellow her son. All that mess crazy 'cause, if I can figure that out, any fool gonna do the same.

Oh shit, that sound like thunder. It sure gonna be a mess for sure if it start raining now. No, honey, don't move. You sit right there like I tell you.

Lottie Mae, ain't this your stop coming up? What time you finish today? Girl, it gonna be dark then; sure hope that boy of yours gonna pick you up. That wife of his at least should let him do that. Well, at least you got your umbrella. Rain come too hard, it gonna flood for sure. Anyhow, look for me tomorrow. You be careful now.

116

Morning, Faye. How you be this morning? I know what you mean. Look like when a body run late ain't no such a thing as catch up. Once I gets to Miss Arnold, I got to catch up on the ironing 'cause, with Mr. Arnold going upstate to some kind of stock meeting, Miss Arnold go pulling out everything to be iron. Don't ask me why, but it seems to me every time Mr. Arnold got to go upstate, Miss Arnold come 'round kind of nervous like to me.

The other week you ask if I seen William. No, not that William to Fanny. We been talking 'bout the one been oversea in Viet Nam, you know the Marine service fellow. When the bus pass that big car lot, I seen him all dress up in a suit and tie, and he been walking 'round some cars with folks following him looking at cars. He look alright to me. They ain't got to know nothing over there where he at. I talk with Vanessa, and she herself tell me when William get back, that place never did give William his old job back. Sure, he been low. How you think all them fellows feel like when they been fighting and come back home to no jobs. Hell, some of them ain't come back to nothing.

William different from most of them fellows sign up with him. He ain't a 'bout to give up. I see him myself, with that tractor that cut grass all crank up ready to cut them folks grass. Who? Patsy? She long gone, honey. When he get back and them checks ain't coming no more, she done up and fly the coop. I know one thing, he must be doing real good 'cause the paper been saying he the number one salesman more than one time. Just 'bout everybody from the church get they cars through William. I hear tell them other folks working over there try to give William trouble at first 'cause our folks, when they get ready to get a car, they ain't been gonna let nobody but William sell them the car.

Sister Ivory tell me Brother Ivory ain't had no notion of buying no car. He just been nosy, wanting to see if it been true William been selling cars on that big car lot. Sister Ivory tell me that when

117

William get through talking and showing Brother Ivory this thing and the next thing 'bout them cars and trucks, shucks, Brother Ivory done sign up to buy a truck. Now, ever since then Brother Ivory is William mouth piece, and ain't nobody like William.

No he ain't, neither. He taking that girl name Darlene out 'cause they been in church together. Well, now, I ain't going so far as to say she all that pretty, but she talk pretty, like she taking time saying every word. Downright friendly, too. How I know? William had her over to meet me when they been at church. She shake my hand and hold it like she mean it. If she pretending, that her business; I just take it upon myself she nice 'cause she stay right there talking with me. I notice she ain't stay with them others she meet long as she stay talking with me.

I don't know 'bout no divorce. All I know is Patsy gone. Look like William gonna make somebody a good catch.

It ain't been easy for William 'cause folks 'round here thinking he be crazy for sure. He been in and out of that veteran hospital. Then, they say some doctor keep looking at his pictures they done take all over William head. I hear say it been just a little piece of them fragment thing been blow up on William, and it been pressing in the head causing William to scream out. They say William had it so bad, them pains been dropping down on him any ol' time. He been working for the city sanitation one time, and it been trash day. They say William start screaming and beating at his own head with some branches he been picking up. Them fellows on the truck grab William to keep the poor fellow from beating the brains out from his own head. That ain't been all; I been over to Sister Ola house.—She the one live right 'cross the road from William Aunt Lovey.—Anyhow, it been in the summertime, and we been on the porch burning the pot to keep the bugs off and just catching up on things when, all of a sudden, this body run out of the house 'cross the road from us, just screaming and screaming down the road. Lord have mercy, the poor man been crazy with pain, and it ain't been nothing we been able to do.

They say that been coming on William day and night 'til that doctor find that piece of thing in William head. He regular now; ain't nothing wrong with William. Folks say William lucky; I say William save by the grace of God. Some of the fellows sure enough done loose they manhood.

Oh, come on, Faye, you know what I mean. The thing get blow off. I ain't saying *who* done lose they thing. Just telling you *some* fellows in this same town done lose they thing. How I know is for me to know, and it ain't for you to know how I find out. You ever know me to lie? You know anybody you and me know can say I done tell a lie? I know that's right. Don't make no sense for me to start lying now at my age.

No, I can't tell you the last time I been over at the towers. I don't look that side no more. Too much drugs and killings over there. I gets tired seeing black faces on the television news trying to hide they faces, with they hands in them cuffs and feet all chain up. Where in the hell is them damn television folks, when them black children get them scholarships and them award things they give out when they do good things in the neighborhood and centers? Where they at when they have them talent shows? Ain't nowhere you gonna find them 'til something bad done gone down.

Sure, I seen your girl on television. I been proud, too, but I still telling you if she ain't been most six foot tall and play ball like a fellow, they ain't been gonna do no reporting on her. No, I ain't saying your daughter Jetta look like no boy. You say that. All I done say is she play ball like them fellows play ball. Ain't that 'bout her last year at that college she done gone to?

What? Girl, I know you lying. Don't tell me no such a thing. How long she been missing? Who she leave with? Linda? But I thought she done marry up with that Sanders boy. Hush your mouth. She ain't missing with the Sanders boy, she missing with the girl Linda he done marry? Now, if that don't take the cake.

You the momma; you got all the right to be upset. All I can say is you done your best, and children now gonna do what make them feel good. Way I see it, it ain't the first time it done happen, and it sure ain't gonna be the last time. You praying every phone ring to be Jetta calling? Don't give up. You just have to pray and hold on to the saying "no news mean good news."

Folks talking? Now, see here; you don't want to get me started on them folks doing the talking. Here, honey. Now, you stop that crying. Wipe your nose. You don't want all these folks on this here bus seeing you down like this.

Hey, driver! Keep them damn eyes on the road. Watch where the hell you driving this damn bus.

See, just like I been telling you, he so damn nosy, he'll wreck this here bus trying to mind your business. Get a hold of yourself now, Faye.

No, go back to your seat, ain't nothing wrong. She done get some trash in the eye. She trying to get it out now. No, we ain't needing no help. What the hell you think I doing?

There now, Faye. You 'bout got it all out? Good.

Oh hell, it raining now, and it 'most time for me to get off. I gonna tell you something, and don't you never forget what I gonna say. You got the troubles, take it to God, pray, and let God handle it for you. See, that where most folks lose the faith. They ain't gonna turn them old loads loose. You just got to make up your mind to let go 'cause some things you ain't gonna change. You can't make folks stop talking, and you can't make no grown woman or man change they life. That got to come from within. Any changes gonna be done, Jetta gonna have to do it. You just keep praying and be ready to tell that girl you love her when she call or when she come home. What you mean, if she want you to come visit her? Ain't no question ought to be in your mind. Get the first thing smoking, and get to that girl.

Sounds like more thunder. Just my luck for the downpour when I got to get off. Sure, I gonna see you tomorrow.

Good morning, Miss Davis. No, don't mind if you do. Sit on down.

Morning, Tommy.

How come I call her Tommy? 'Cause that is Tommy. Listen, Miss Davis I ain't into nobody business, but when I done baby-sit these here children, done change the diapers, and done spread them behinds to clean them good and clean, I know if I cleaning a boy child or a girl child.

Now, I know Tommy must be 'bout thirty-seven, if he a day older, and I been the one to keep him when his momma Inez been working uptown at that cleaners place, and he ain't been no more than six or seven months old then. He been a boy child then, and I ain't concern 'bout what you or nobody else say. He a man now.

He turn *gay*? Well, you call it what you want; I ain't getting into if they gay, sad, or happy. I just know I done take care of him when he been a little one, and I still say I ain't seen nothing 'bout his private parts saying he a girl and ain't a boy back then. That same fellow Tommy been in my house with me taking care of him 'til he get 'bout five years old. Inez bring that boy child to me, and she take a boy child from my care. Sure, folks do what they want to do. If Tommy want to dress up in a dress and say he a girl, that well be his business, and I sure gonna mind my business, but I ain't calling him by no other name.

Miss Davis, you wrong now. Tommy nice. He real nice, and I ain't saying a thing bad 'bout him. How you know ain't nobody in *your* family like Tommy? Well, I can tell you right now, from what I see from some of them same folks in your family you call straight, I like Tommy much more. I ain't gonna sit here and let you try to put in my mouth what I think 'bout Tommy. I saying here and now, he just as good as you and me is 'cause he one of God children, but that don't mean I gonna close my eyes to the fact that he ain't no girl.

I ain't never had no need for folks to tell me what I think. I don't need no thinking in cases like this; I just come out and tell you what is. I ain't too old to know that clothes don't change what folks is. You put a mink on a skunk, you still got a skunk. Ain't no need for you to turn up your nose 'cause every word I done say is true. Tommy ain't like some of these folks getting on this here bus. He always show respect and talk to folks. Not you? You ever wonder why he ain't never say nothing to you? I ain't into saying much to you, neither. Why? 'Cause you ain't a nice person, Miss Davis.

What you mean, how dare me? I been watching you. You don't speak to half the folks on this here bus. You ain't never sit by Tommy, and you sure as hell ain't never look at Tommy like he living. Why you riding this bus? Why Tommy riding this bus? Why I riding this bus? 'Cause we ain't got no choice. We all is going to work, and we all is got to work.

All these years I been riding this bus I done seen a lot of changes take place. I done seen the high fall low and the low go on to higher ground. And, Miss Davis, if it been left up to folks like you, Tommy sure ain't gonna be riding this bus to work.

Sure, he working. He ain't sitting 'round waiting for somebody to take care of him. If them folks down on the job thinking he a girl, that be well for Tommy 'cause he sure been on that same job close to most ten years now. I know everybody riding this bus, black, white, mix, and a few passing, and just a few still pretending I ain't here.

I ain't pointing my finger at nobody 'cause, when my time come die, ain't no way I gonna get lock out of heaven 'cause I done harm to somebody. Time shorter than we think, and I sure as hell ain't gonna be caught mad at nobody. My spirit leave this ol' body, and it gonna fly away happy.

And this here my stop. Hey, everybody back there, see you folks tomorrow, God willing. Don't forget now, a job is a job and *just* a job. Ha ha ha ha ha.

Epilogue

I told the officer in charge of the investigation that, as Minnie stood up, she yelled at everybody on the bus, especially those sitting in the back, saying she would see us the next day. She said not to forget that a job was just a job. Then, she laughed real loud as she was stepping off the bus.

He asked why would Minnie say that about a job. I tried to explain to him that a person would have to really know Minnie and be a rider on that bus in order to understand how she and others related to the different moods of frustration, anticipation, hatred, and jealousy that rode along every day on the bus. Each rider had his or her own hell or heaven to think about on the way to work. I believe that Minnie just had a way of telling people how to make the most out of a bad situation.

I honestly don't believe that she intended to ever hurt anyone. She saw a spade as a spade and only made judgement statements when it cleared her position, not only on the bus, but in her neighborhood and church. She had a way of telling everybody that they were important, and that no matter what type of work a person did, it was only a job and always give the best. In another way, Minnie was telling all on the bus that we did not *live* the job, we only *worked* it, and at the end of the day, we would each return to our own world.

Oh yes, I told the officer I saw Minnie laugh loud looking at the driver. She never said a word to him. That was Minnie's way. When she turned her mind away from you after telling you what she wanted to say, everybody that knew Minnie would tell you that she was finished with that.

I remember her stepping off the bus. The bus jerked, and the driver drove off, but the door was not completely closed. I heard screams. I saw people on the sidewalk waving their hands and running along the bus. The driver must have gone about half of the block before he jerked the bus to a stop.

He never moved out of the driver's seat. He did not move to open the door. I don't know who opened the door, but it was not the driver. There were so many people around the outside, it was difficult for those on the bus to get off. The school crossing guard, a retired policeman, took over and ordered everybody to move away. I heard sirens in the distance. My Lord, where did all the people come from?

I was pushed away from the bus. Looking back, I saw a foot without a shoe under the bus, near the front by the steps. Farther back, almost in the middle of the bus, was a heap of something, red and mud mixed with pieces of brown material. I screamed. What was left of Minnie's brown coat was entangled with what was left of Minnie. I fainted.

I often heard Minnie talk about her Reverend South and the choir at her church. Somehow at the funeral, Minnie must have placed a spiritual hand on him, and her spirit sang with the choir because, even in death, Minnie never did lie. Her Reverend South's compassionate words lifted all souls, and had even me on my feet praising God for the life and homegoing of Minnie.

Looking around the church, I recognized Mr. and Mrs. Arnold right away. They were holding hands, and their heads were bowed in a sorrow that no one in that church would ever dare to question. Later I was told that the spray that covered Minnie's casket was purchased by the Arnolds.

At the end of the service, I saw a tall, distinguished looking man walking slowly up the aisle of the church, staring straight

126

ahead with his eyes directly on the casket. His eyes did not move left or right. He walked upright with slow, deliberate steps, as if he was on a mission. The way he walked demanded attention; it seemed as if all eyes were on him. I watched as he approached the casket. He bowed his head very low and looked upon Minnie's face for what seemed like a long, searching minute. Then, he took his right hand and placed it on the casket. His left hand patted Minnie's hair and slowly touched her face. His shoulders shook, as if he was fighting to control deep emotions, to hold on to what strength he had left.

He turned slowly, then looked toward where Minnie's family was sitting, and I saw on the man's face lines running in red, raised, healed scars which disfigured over half of the face on one side. All of a sudden I knew that the man standing by the casket looking at Minnie's family was the husband that Minnie put out years before. I understand that it was a terrible fight on a Sunday morning when he tried to stop Minnie from going to church. I think the people said his name was Albert.

As he moved to walk toward the back of the church, he stumbled a little down the aisle. I saw tears roll down his face, and he used the back of his hand to wipe the tears away. He was a broken man leaving the church. He looked neither right nor left as he went, and no one said a word to him as he quietly stumbled out of the church.

As always, people will talk. Minnie was buried on the third day after her death, and everybody riding the bus on the following days talked about how Minnie would have enjoyed hearing Reverend South preach her funeral.

If the driver is charged with driving under the influence of drugs, time will tell because now we wait for the court hearing, and the cross town bus rolls on.

About the Author

Katie B. Catalon is in her twenty-third year as a cosmetology teacher for the Charleston County school district in North Charleston, South Carolina. She attended the College of Charleston and has performed course work at Clemson University, South Carolina State University, the Citadel, and Charleston Southern University (formerly the Baptist College).

She is the owner of Catalon's Hair Styling Salon, as well as being the recording secretary for the National Beauty Culturists' League, Incorporated, and the vice president of the South Carolina State Cosmetologist Association. Additionally, she holds memberships in numerous professional organizations including: the National Education Association, the Charleston County Education Association, the South Carolina Active Teachers' Association, the South Carolina Vocational Teachers' Association, the South Carolina Registered Cosmetologists Association, and the Gamma Xi Omega chapter of Alpha Kappa Alpha National Sorority.